An Introductory Guide to

Anatomy & Physiology

Louise Tucker

General Editor Jane Foulston

HOLISTIC THERAPY

BOOKS

Published by Holistic Therapy Books
An imprint of Ruben Publishing Ltd.
P.O. Box 270, Cambridge, CB1 2XE
01223 500344

First published March 2000
Second impression October 2000
Third impression October 2001
Second edition October 2002
Reprinted October 2003

ISBN 1-903348-04-8.

Set in 10/13 Legacy.

Printed by Scotprint.

Prepared for the publishers by The Write Idea, Cambridge.

Publisher's note
The phenomenal success of the first edition of this book has given us the opportunity to improve the text and illustrations with each new impression. Improvements have been suggested by lecturers who have pointed out inconsistencies and places where clarity could be improved.

For this second edition the muscle illustrations in Chapter 4 have been completely redrawn and some of the captions made clearer.

Lecturers should always cross reference the syllabus from which they are teaching to the contents of each chapter as different examination boards have different requirements and an introductory guide cannot fully cover every aspect of such a complex subject as Anatomy and Physiology. The publishers are grateful to those lecturers who have been good enough to write in with suggestions.

We would also like to thank Anne Wadmore for her invaluable assistance in the preparation of the new muscle illustrations.

ANATOMY AND PHYSIOLOGY

Contents

Introduction

This book provides an introduction to the anatomy and physiology of the body. An understanding of anatomy and physiology is essential for all those working in beauty therapy, complementary therapy, sports therapy, nursing and paramedicine. When treating patients and clients, knowledge of the structure and function of the various systems of the body ensures that the correct treatment is administered and contra-indications are recognised. Professionals, as well as ITEC, CIDESCO, CIBTAC, Edexcel, City and Guilds and NVQ students will find it an invaluable learning and reference tool.

Author

Louise Tucker

Louise Tucker is a freelance writer and teacher. She has written and published several books and articles.

General editor

Jane Foulston

Jane Foulston has had a long career as a lecturer in anatomy and physiology for beauty and complementary therapy in private and FE colleges as well as setting up a therapy school in Japan. She also has 15 years' experience as an external examiner for professional vocational qualifications. She lectured at East Berkshire College and Bridgewater College and her students have become practitioners in beauty therapy, aromatherapy and in a variety of sports therapies. She is currently Director of the International Therapy Examination Council.

Contributing editors

Marguerite Wynne

Marguerite Wynne began her career in one of London's foremost beauty salons and went on to teach in The College of Beauty Therapy in the West End. Subsequently, she owned her own clinic and school in Buckinghamshire, specialising in Complementary Therapies. She has been a Chief Examiner for ITEC since 1985 during which time she spent three years based in the Far East.

Jill Wilshaw

Jill Wilshaw qualified in Beauty Therapy in 1980. Initially she worked in a top London Slimming Clinic before opening up her own highly successful home visiting practice in and around Harrogate. During this time she started her own private school teaching mainly Anatomy, Physiology and Massage. After relocating to Aberdeen she lectured in many subjects relating to Beauty, Complementary and Sports Therapies at Aberdeen College. She has been a Senior Examiner for ITEC in both practical and theory since 1983.

Sheila Cunningham

Sheila Cunningham is a Senior Lecturer at the School of Health, Biological and Environmental Sciences, Middlesex University. She is a qualified nurse and teaches on a variety of courses including Sports Performance Therapy, Traditional Chinese Medicine and Nursing.

Key to anatomical language

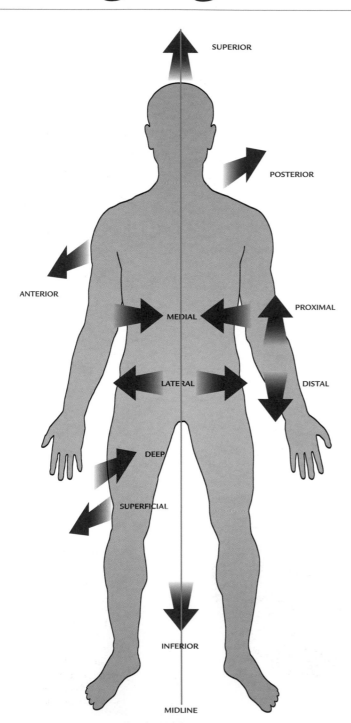

SUPERIOR

POSTERIOR

ANTERIOR

MEDIAL

PROXIMAL

LATERAL

DISTAL

DEEP

SUPERFICIAL

INFERIOR

MIDLINE

Anatomy means the study of the body's structure. In order to avoid confusion when referring to parts of the body, it is necessary to have a standardised system of anatomical descriptions and positions. The definitions used on diagrams are explained below. All of these terms refer to what is known as the standard anatomical position: the body is standing erect, facing the observer, with arms extended and the palms of the hands facing forwards (see diagram). Learning these terms will help you to understand the diagrams in the book as well as help you describe your own.

Anterior: towards front
Deep: further from surface
Distal: furthest from source
External: outer
Inferior: towards lower part
Internal: inner
Lateral: away from midline
Medial: towards midline
Midline: line through midline of the body from front to back
Posterior: towards rear
Proximal: nearest source
Superficial: near surface
Superior: towards upper part

The Cell

The cell is the basis of all life. To understand the structure and function of the body, we need to understand the structure and function of its tiniest part – the cell.

In Brief

A cell is the smallest unit of matter that can live independently and reproduce itself. Cells exist in all shapes and sizes — elongated, square, star-shaped and oval — and have many different functions. A group of cells form tissue. The study of the structure and form of cells and tissues is called histology.

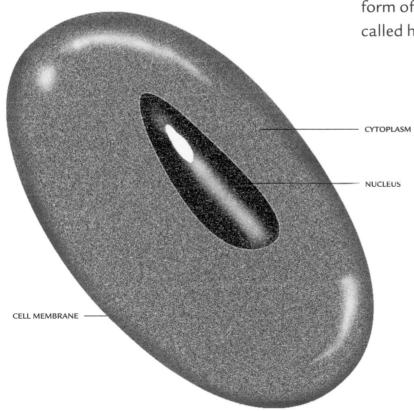

CYTOPLASM

NUCLEUS

CELL MEMBRANE

A SINGLE CELL (GENERALISED)

STRUCTURE

What is a cell made of?

Protoplasm, a slightly opaque, colourless jelly-like substance. It is 70% water plus

- organic and inorganic salts
- carbohydrates
- lipids (fatty substance)
- nitrogenous substances; these are amino acids obtained from protein
- compounds of all of the above substances.

What does a cell look like?

The diagram below is of a generalised cell, i.e. it shows you all the parts that exist in different types of cell. It is meant as a guide not as an exact replica. The cell is a living structure, thus it is only possible to show a general picture. It is worth remembering that cells constantly move and change.

THE CELL AND ITS ORGANELLES

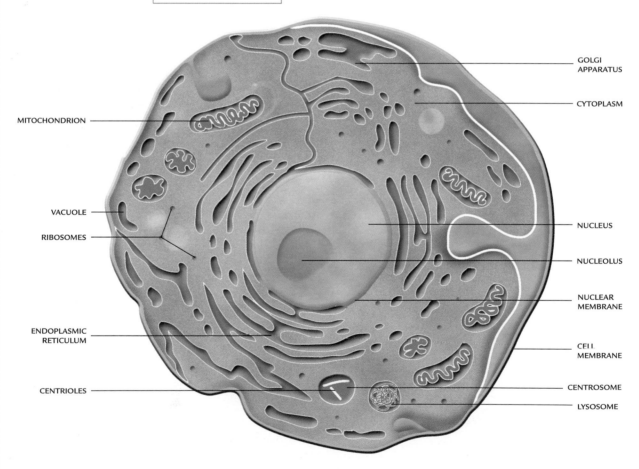

MITOCHONDRION

VACUOLE

RIBOSOMES

ENDOPLASMIC RETICULUM

CENTRIOLES

GOLGI APPARATUS

CYTOPLASM

NUCLEUS

NUCLEOLUS

NUCLEAR MEMBRANE

CELL MEMBRANE

CENTROSOME

LYSOSOME

The following list explains the function of all the structures named on the diagram on page 8.

Cell membrane

A fine membrane, made of protein threads and lipids (fats), which has two functions: to keep the nucleus and the cytoplasm in the cell but to let other substances, like fats and proteins, out. It works as a filter between the fluid inside the cell and the tissue fluid outside it. Some substances can cross this membrane but others are blocked. Substances go in and out of cells in several different ways:

● **diffusion**: the membrane has tiny holes, or pores, between its proteins and lipids through which small molecules, like oxygen and carbon dioxide, can pass.

DIFFUSION

CELL (SEMI-PERMEABLE) MEMBRANE

WEAK CONCENTRATION EQUAL CONCENTRATION

STRONG CONCENTRATION

● **osmosis**: the process of transferring water across the membrane by osmotic pressure — when the concentration or pressure of a solution is greater on one side of the membrane, water passes through to that side and vice versa until the concentration is equal on both

sides. When both sides of the membrane have solutions of the same pressure, it is called isotonic pressure.

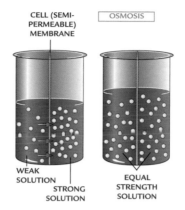

CELL (SEMI-PERMEABLE) MEMBRANE   OSMOSIS

WEAK SOLUTION   EQUAL STRENGTH SOLUTION

STRONG SOLUTION

● **dissolution (or dissolving)**: fatty substances are too big to diffuse through the membrane's tiny pores, so they dissolve into the fatty or lipid part of the membrane.

DISSOLUTION

CELL (SEMI-PERMEABLE) MEMBRANE

FATTY SUBSTANCE   FATTY SUBSTANCE DISSOLVED IN MEMBRANE

● **active transport**: when substances are too large to pass directly through the membrane, or are not soluble in fat, a carrier substance in the cell membrane takes them from the outside to the inside. Glucose and amino acids are both transferred by active transport. It is active because energy is used.

ACTIVE TRANSPORT

CELL (SEMI-PERMEABLE) MEMBRANE

LARGE MOLECULE

● **filtration**: the movement of water and soluble substances across a membrane caused by the difference in pressure either side of the membrane. The force of a fluid's weight pushes against a surface and the fluid is thus moved through the membrane. This is called hydro-static pressure which is the process responsible for the formation of urine in the kidneys. Waste products are filtered out of the blood into the kidney tubules because of a difference in hydrostatic pressure.

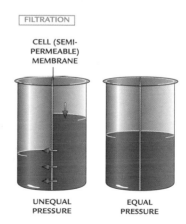

FILTRATION

CELL (SEMI-PERMEABLE) MEMBRANE

UNEQUAL PRESSURE   EQUAL PRESSURE

Cytoplasm

Cytoplasm is the protoplasm inside the cell but outside the nucleus. It contains several different structures and substances:

Mitochondria

These organelles (little organs) are sometimes referred to as the 'power houses' of the cell, since they supply the cell with energy. Cell survival depends upon the chemical reactions that take place within the mitochondria, which result in a release of energy and the formation of ATP (adenosine triphosphate), the main energy transporter within the cell.

Endoplasmic reticulum

A network of membranes that forms a system of sacs and canals through the cytoplasm of a cell. It forms the circulation of the cell, allowing the movement of different substances.

Ribosomes

The 'protein factories' of a cell. They produce enzymes and other protein compounds; protein is used for the growth and repair of a cell.

Lysosomes

These organelles contain digestive enzymes which destroy worn-out parts of a cell and bacteria. They break down parts of food allowing them to be used for energy transfer within the cell.

Vacuoles

These are empty spaces within the cytoplasm. They contain waste materials or secretions formed by the cytoplasm and are used for storage or digestion purposes in different kinds of cells.

Golgi apparatus

The golgi apparatus combines polysaccharides (carbohydrates) with protein compounds and secretes these in order to send them to other parts of the cell for use as energy. It is a communication network from deep within the cell to its membrane.

Centrioles

These are paired, rod-like organelles that lie at right angles to each other. They are made of fine tubules which play an important role in mitosis (cell reproduction).

Centrosomes

Dense areas of cytoplasm containing the centrioles.

Nucleus

The very centre of the cell, the nucleus controls every organelle within the cytoplasm, and the processes of cell growth, repair and reproduction. It is contained within the nuclear membrane and its special protoplasm is called nucleoplasm. It contains DNA (deoxyribonucleic acid) which carries the cell's genetic code and chromatin, the material needed to form chromosomes. Chromosomes are made up of connected strands of DNA molecules, known as genes. A gene is therefore part of the length of a DNA molecule.
Chromosomes carry inherited information which makes sure that when cells divide the 'daughter cells' are identical to the 'parent cells'. Each species is determined by the number of chromosomes in the nucleus. Human cells contain 46, i.e. 23 from each parent.

Chromatids

Two strands of chromatids held together by a centromere form a chromosome.

Centromere

The point where the two chromatids join in the chromosome.

Nucleolus

A small body within the nucleus that programmes the formation of ribosomes which then move into the cytoplasm of the cell and produce protein.

You now know the structure of a cell and the names of all its different parts. The next sections explain how cells function and reproduce.

FUNCTION

What does a cell do?

It lives! The human body is made of cells, which form organs, tissues, and fluid. Blood, for example, is a liquid tissue made of several different types of cells. What a cell does is reproduced on a larger scale throughout the body and throughout human life: breathing, digesting, excreting, reproducing, sensing, growing, moving, dying. When a cell goes wrong, the body goes wrong, since cell breakdown, and a subsequent inability to perform its usual functions, is the origin of disease and illness.

If you want to understand a cell's relationship to the rest of the body think of this:

- a group of cells of similar type and function join to form a tissue

- a group of tissues of related function join to form an organ (e.g. stomach, lung, heart)

- a group of organs of related function join to form a system (e.g. digestive, respiratory, vascular)

- a group of systems join together to form an organism (e.g. a human body).

Summary of functions

- *Respiration: this is controlled absorption of oxygen that combines with nutrients in an oxidative reaction. This results in energy production and the formation of ATP. The waste produced is carbon dioxide.*
- *Growth: cells grow and repair themselves by making protein.*
- *Excretion: waste which might be harmful to the cell in large amounts, e.g. urea or carbon dioxide, is removed.*
- *Movement: whole cells, like blood cells, can move and parts of cells move, like the cilia of ciliated cells, but only in one direction.*
- *Reproduction: all cells grow to maturity and the majority then reproduce themselves. This can be simple cell division (mitosis) or sexual reproduction (meiosis).*
- *Metabolism: the chemical reactions that occur inside the cell.*
  - *Anabolism: the chemical activity involved in the process of making new products (usually proteins) for growth and repair.*
  - *Catabolism: the chemical activity involved in the breakdown of substances into simple forms, which results in the production of energy and waste. The energy is used to perform various cell functions.*
- *Sensitivity: cells are able to respond to stimuli, which can be mechanical, electrical, thermal or chemical.*

CELL REPRODUCTION

How do cells grow/reproduce?

Through mitosis. It is vital for living things to reproduce themselves in order to continue life. Since the human body is made of cells, these cells must reproduce in order for the body to continue living. Mitosis is the multiplication of cells i.e. the constant process of making new cells in order for life to continue when the old cells die. This continues throughout life, except in the case of nerve cells, which are not always replaced when they die. Mitosis is faster in children and slows in later life. The process takes approximately two hours. If cells continue to divide and multiply they can create tumours and sometimes cancer. There are four stages of mitosis:

1 Prophase

- The centrosome divides into two centrioles. These move away from each other, though still joined by the spindle-like threads of the centrosome.
- Towards the end of the prophase the chromatin in the cell's nucleus shortens and thickens, forming into visible pairs of rods called chromosomes (made of condensed chromatin and DNA).
- Each chromosome consists of two chromatids joined by a centromere.
- The nucleolus disappears.

2 Metaphase

- The nuclear membrane of the nucleus disappears.
- The chromosomes arrange themselves at the centre of the cell, each attached to the spindle by its centromere.
- By the end of the metaphase, each individual chromosome can be seen distinctly as two chromatids starting to pull apart.

3 Anaphase

- The centromere stretches as the centrioles are drawn further apart.
- Pairs of chromatids divide and identical halves of the pairs move to each end of the cell.
- At the end of the anaphase, the spindle threads of the centrioles divide to form

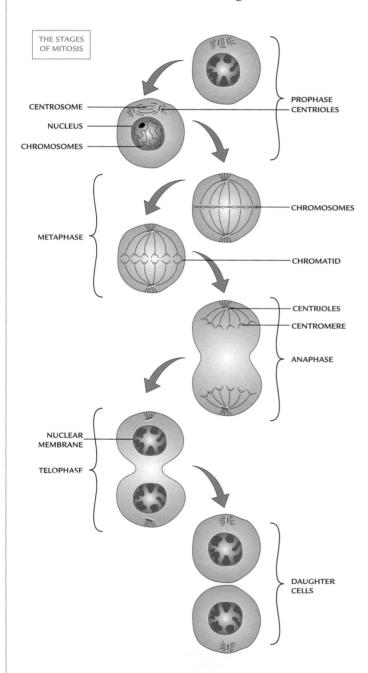

THE STAGES OF MITOSIS

PROPHASE

CENTROSOME
NUCLEUS
CHROMOSOMES
CENTRIOLES

METAPHASE

CHROMOSOMES

CHROMATID

CENTRIOLES
CENTROMERE

ANAPHASE

NUCLEAR MEMBRANE

TELOPHASE

DAUGHTER CELLS

new centromeres and the cell membrane begins to constrict in the centre.

4 *Telophase*
- A new nuclear membrane appears around each set of chromosomes.
- The spindle fibres disintegrate and the centrioles replicate.
- The cell membrane continues to constrict until two cells are formed. These two daughter cells will be identical copies of the original single parent cell. Eventually, the daughter cells will also divide and the whole process continues throughout life.

Interphase
- The cell is resting.

- DNA is reproduced just before mitosis occurs.
- Nuclear protein is synthesised.
- Cell increases in size.

Meiosis
This is the cell reproduction which results in a gamete/sex cell. In meiosis, only half the numbers of chromosomes are present, 23 in the male sperm and 23 in the female ovum. When a male sperm fuses with a female ovum they create a zygote, a single complete cell with 46 chromosomes. The zygote will divide by mitosis and the organism that results from the cell division is called an embryo.

You now know the structure and function of cells and how they reproduce. The following section explains the different tissues made from cells found in the body.

TISSUE TYPES MADE FROM CELLS

Cells make tissue. There are four types of tissue: epithelial, connective, nervous and muscular.

Epithelial tissue
(also known as epithelium)
There are two categories of epithelial tissue, simple and compound. Simple epithelium usually functions as a covering or lining for organs and vessels whereas compound provides external protection and internal elasticity. Goblet cells are often found in simple epithelium. These cells secrete mucus.

Simple epithelium
Simple epithelium consists of a single layer of cells attached to a basement membrane. There are four types: squamous or pavement, cuboidal, columnar and ciliated.

Squamous
Structure: single layer of flattened cells attached to a basement membrane
Function: forms a smooth lining for the heart, blood and lymph vessels and alveoli of the lungs.

SQUAMOUS

Cuboidal
Structure: single layer of cube-shaped cells attached to a basement membrane.
Function: forms lining of kidney tubules as well as some glands; can secrete substances and absorb them.

CUBOIDAL

Columnar

Structure: single layer of tall, rectangular cells attached to a basement membrane; resilient.

Function: forms lining in very active parts of the body such as the stomach, intestines and urethra; some of the cells secrete mucus and some absorb mucus, depending on where they are in the body.

COLUMNAR

Ciliated

Structure: single layer of mostly columnar cells (sometimes combined with squamous or cuboidal cells) attached to a basement membrane. Tiny hair-like projections, or cilia, stick out from the cell membrane.

Function: the cilia work in waves, all moving together in the same direction. They help to remove mucus, foreign matter and debris, keeping passageways and linings clear. The respiratory system is lined with these cells.

CILIATED COLUMNAR

Compound epithelium

Compound epithelium has many layers of cells and no basement membrane. It is formed from a combination of deep layers of columnar cells plus flatter cells towards the surface. It protects delicate parts of the body. There are two types: stratified and transitional.

Stratified

● *Keratinised (dry)*

Structure: compound epithelium with dry surface cells; forms a dead layer e.g. hair, skin, nails. It is keratinised (i.e. the surface layer has dried out into keratin, a fibrous protein which creates a waterproof layer). Skin is stratified, keratinised, squamous epithelium.

Function: the keratinisation prevents deeper layers from drying out and protects them.

● *Non-keratinised (wet)*

Structure: compound epithelium with wet surface cells e.g. inside mouth, lining of oesophagus, conjunctiva (mucous membrane) of eyes.

Function: provides lubrication.

STRATIFIED

Transitional

Structure: similar to stratified epithelium except that the surface cells are not flattened and thus can change shape when necessary; cube-shaped surface cells and deeper pear-shaped cells.

Function: found in organs that need waterproof and expandable lining e.g. bladder and ureters.

TRANSITIONAL

Nervous tissue

Structure: arranged in bundles of fibres, composed of nerve cells and neuroglia. The cells have long fibrous processes. On a nerve cell these processes are called dendrites and axons.

Function: capable of transmitting signals to and from the brain; protective.

Muscular tissue

There are three types of muscle tissue:
- striated or voluntary
- smooth or involuntary
- cardiac.

Structure: all muscle is made of 75% water, 20% protein, 5% mineral salts, glycogen, glucose and fat.

Function:

skeletal: to help support and move the body;

smooth: to carry out involuntary functions, e.g. peristalsis;

cardiac: heart muscle to pump blood.

Connective tissue

Connective tissues are the supporting tissues of the body; they have mostly mechanical functions and connect more active tissues (like bones and muscles).

Structure: can be semi-solid, solid or liquid; can have fibres present or not.

Function: mainly mechanical connecting other more active tissues.

There are eight types:

- areolar
- adipose
- lymphoid
- yellow elastic
- white fibrous
- bone
- blood
- cartilage.

Areolar

This is loose connective tissue, the most general connective tissue found in the human body.

Structure: semi-solid and permeable thus allowing fluids to pass through; it contains yellow elastic and white fibres as well as fibrocytes and mast cells which produce histamine (protection) and heparin (anti-coagulant, prevents clotting).

Function: found all over the body connecting and supporting other tissues e.g. under the skin, between muscles, supporting blood vessels and nerves and in the alimentary canal.

Adipose

This is also known as fatty tissue.

Structure: made up of fat cells containing fat globules; found between muscle fibres and, with areolar tissue, under the skin giving the body a smooth, continuous outline; also found around the kidneys and the back of the eyes.

Function: protective and insulatory properties: helps retain body heat because it is a poor conductor of heat; also a food reserve.

Lymphoid

Structure: semi-solid tissue; has some white fibres but not in bundles; lots of cells, the majority are lymphocytes and reticular cells which have a disease control function – the cell engulfs bacteria and destroys it.

Function: forms lymphatic system cells and blood cells and thus protects against disease; found in lymph nodes, thymus, the spleen, the tonsils, in the wall of the large intestine, the appendix and the glands of the small intestine.

Yellow elastic

Structure: mainly composed of elastic fibres and very few cells; this tissue is capable of considerable extension and recoil.

Function: to enable stretch and recoil e.g. forms lung tissue, bronchi and trachea, arteries especially the large ones, stomach, bladder and any other organs that need to stretch and recoil.

Useful Tip

The easiest way to see a cilia is to look inside your nostrils. What we call nostril hairs are in fact cilia, which prevent debris and mucus from blocking our breathing.

White fibrous

Structure: strongly connective but not very elastic; consists mainly of closely packed bundles of collagen fibres with only a few cells in rows between the fibres; the fibres run in the same direction.

Function: connection and protection of parts of the body e.g. forms ligaments and the periosteum of bone; forms the outer protection of organs e.g. around the kidneys, the dura of the brain, the fascia of muscles and the tendons.

Bone

Structure: hardest structure in the body; two types, compact and cancellous – compact is dense bone for strength, cancellous for structure bearing and cellular development; composition of bone is 25% water, 30% organic material, 45% inorganic salts.

Function: to support and protect the body and all its organs, as well as produce cells in bone marrow.

Blood

Structure: fluid connective tissue, containing 45% cells and 55% plasma. Cell content is erythrocytes (red blood cells), leucocytes (white blood cells) and thrombocytes (platelets).

Function: to transport food and oxygen to all the cells of the body and to remove waste from them (erythrocytes), to fight infection (leucocytes) and to clot (thrombocytes).

Cartilage

Structure: firm, tough tissue; solid and contains cells called chondrocytes; there are three types:

Hyaline

Structure: bluish-white, smooth; chondrocyte cells are grouped together in nests in a solid matrix; particularly resilient.

Function: connecting and protecting: found on articular surfaces of joints i.e. parts of bone which form joints; forms costal cartilages and parts of the larynx, trachea and bronchi.

Yellow elastic cartilage

Structure: yellow elastic fibres running through a solid matrix. Contains fibrocyte and chondrocyte cells which lie between multidirectional fibres.

Function: flexibility; found in parts of the body that need to move freely like the pinna (cartilage part of the ear) and epiglottis.

White fibrocartilage

Structure: white fibres closely packed in dense masses; contains chondrocyte cells; extremely tough and slightly flexible.

Function: to absorb shock e.g. it forms intervertebral discs as well as the semi-lunar cartilages, the shock absorbers positioned between the articulating surfaces of the knee joint bones; also found in hip and shoulder sockets.

● SUMMARY

The cell:
- *is a microscopic building block*
- *is a microcosm of body functions: ingesting, excreting, breathing, reproducing, moving, dying*
- *reproduces by division*
- *makes tissues; there are four main tissue types in the body.*

The Skin

The skin is an outer
protective layer, also
known as an integument.

In Brief
The skin is the largest organ
(group of tissues). It covers
the whole body and is water-
resistant. There are two layers:
the epidermis and the dermis.
It has many functions including
protecting and shaping the
body.

CROSS-SECTION OF SKIN

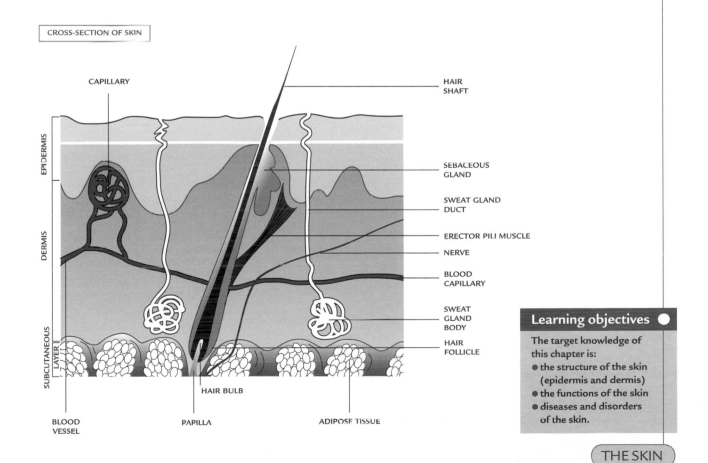

CAPILLARY

HAIR
SHAFT

EPIDERMIS

SEBACEOUS
GLAND

SWEAT GLAND
DUCT

DERMIS

ERECTOR PILI MUSCLE

NERVE

BLOOD
CAPILLARY

SWEAT
GLAND
BODY

SUBCUTANEOUS
LAYER

HAIR
FOLLICLE

HAIR BULB

BLOOD
VESSEL

PAPILLA

ADIPOSE TISSUE

Learning objectives

The target knowledge of
this chapter is:
- the structure of the skin
  (epidermis and dermis)
- the functions of the skin
- diseases and disorders
  of the skin.

THE SKIN

STRUCTURE

What is the epidermis?

The epidermis is the layer of skin that we can see. It varies in thickness, depending on the part of the body e.g. it is thickest on the soles of the feet and palms of the hand and thinnest on eyelids and nipples. The cells on the surface are constantly coming off (shedding): this is called desquamation. They are also constantly replaced from below as cells in the basal layer of the epidermis multiply and are pushed up to the surface. There is no blood supply to the epidermis, hardly any nerve supply and it receives nutrients and fluids from the lymphatic vessels in the dermis. In total there are five layers in the epidermis.

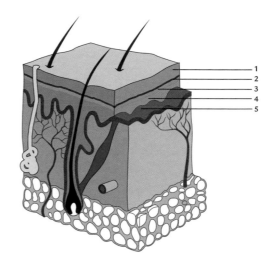

1. STRATUM CORNEUM
2. STRATUM LUCIDUM
3. STRATUM GRANULOSUM
4. STRATUM SPINOSUM
5. STRATUM GERMINATIVUM
    – BASAL

Structure of epidermis

1. **Stratum corneum – surface**
- hardened, flattened dead cells
- constantly being shed – desquamation
- cell membrane is not visible.

2. **Stratum lucidum – clear layer**
- denucleated cells but not completely hard
- most easily visible under a microscope (only on palms and soles)
- cell membranes becoming visible.

3. **Stratum granulosum – granular layer**
- cells have a distinct nucleus but cell membranes are dying
- contain granules which are visible in healing tissue after trauma.

4. **Stratum spinosum – prickle cell layer**
- cells are living and membranes are intact; they have fibrils which interlock
- capable of mitosis under friction or pressure i.e. on soles of feet or palms of hands.

5. **Stratum germinativum – basal layer**
- the primary site of cell division/ reproduction (mitosis) in the skin
- cells are living. It is in this layer that cells are made. They take about 28–30 days to move up from here through the five layers of the epidermis before being shed.
- this layer contains a pigment known as melanin that gives skin its natural colour, whether red, yellow or black. Melanin is produced by cells called melanocytes.

What is the dermis?

The dermis is commonly known as the true skin. Unlike the epidermis, this layer is connected to the blood and lymph supply as well as the nerves. The dermis contains sweat and sebaceous glands, hair follicles and many living cells.

Structure of dermis

● made of connective tissue, mainly areolar tissue which is tough and elastic.
● contains white collagen fibres and yellow elastic tissue known as elastin. Collagen plumps the skin and elastin keeps it supple and elastic. Both diminish with age.

Dermis contains

1. **Specialised cells**
● **fibroblasts**: responsible for the production of areolar tissue, collagen and elastin. Fibroblasts can be damaged by ultraviolet light.
● **mast cells**: produce histamine as an allergic response and heparin, an anti-coagulant
● **histiocytes**: also produce histamine
● **leucocytes**: white blood cells which help to fight infection and disease.

2. **Nerve endings**: alert the brain and thus the body to heat, cold, pressure and pain. These are part of the defence system of the body.

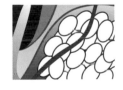

3. **Sweat glands**: these stretch from deep in the dermis to the outer layer of the epidermis; there are two kinds –

● **eccrine**: these excrete watery sweat and control body temperature. Found all over the body especially on the palms of the hands and the soles of the feet.
● **apocrine**: these excrete milky fluid. Body odour is produced when the sweat from these glands mixes with bacteria on the surface of the skin. Found in the groin and axillae (armpits).

Sweat contains mainly water, urea and salts (mostly sodium chloride).

4. **Hair follicles**: travel through the epidermis and the dermis. Tiny muscles, called erector pili, are attached to each hair and help with temperature control of the body by pulling the hair upright and trapping a layer of air – goose pimples.

5. **Sebaceous glands**: connected with hair follicles. They produce sebum, a fatty acid which keeps the skin moist and which lubricates the hair shaft and they are therefore found in hairy areas, not on the palms of the hands or soles of the feet.

Sweat and sebum combine on the surface of the skin to form the acid mantle, a protective shield which helps to control bacteria levels and prevents infections and disease and also acts as a natural moisturiser. The pH balance of the skin is 5.6-6.5 and this acid environment helps to prevent bacterial growth.

6. **Blood supply**: a system of blood vessels including microscopic capillaries which are one cell thick.

7. **Lymphatic capillary**: works in conjunction with the blood supply.

8. **Papilla**: small conical projections at the base of the hair containing blood vessels and nerves which

supply the hair with nutrients.

You now know the structure of both layers of the skin. The following section describes the skin's functions.

FUNCTIONS

The skin has eight main functions:

- **Secretion**: secretes sebum
- **Heat regulation**: cools and warms body
- **Absorption**: of drugs or essential oils
- **Protection**: keeps out bacteria and creates barrier against rays of the sun
- **Elimination**: of waste products
- **Sensation**: skin is the organ of touch
- **Vitamin D** production
- **Melanin** production.

Secretion

The skin secretes sebum from the sebaceous glands. This fatty substance lubricates the hair shafts and when combined with perspiration on the surface of the skin, it creates a natural moisturiser which acts as a protective barrier against bacteria.

Heat regulation

Body temperature is maintained in healthy humans at 36.8°C. Organs involved in heat production are the muscles, liver and digestive organs. Heat is absorbed and maintained in the subcutaneous layer of adipose tissue. Heat regulation is controlled in the following ways:

Cooling
- **Vasodilation**: when the body becomes hot, the capillaries dilate allowing more blood to reach the surface of the skin. The pores dilate allowing the heat to be lost from the body. This causes the skin to flush – this is known

as hyperaemia. Sweating will occur simultaneously and the evaporation of perspiration from the surface has a cooling effect on the body.

Warming
- **Vasoconstriction**: when cold, the body protects itself by moving blood from the extremities to the major organs, thus ensuring that they are kept warm. With the blood diverted to the deeper parts of the body, the capillaries contract as do the pores. As a result, the skin appears pale and heat loss is inhibited.

  The erector pili muscles contract causing body hair to stand on end, trapping air against the surface of the skin, which is then warmed by body heat.

  Shivering occurs, caused by rapid and repeated muscle contractions which work to raise body temperature.

Absorption

The skin is a waterproof covering but some chemical substances, such as drugs and essential oils, can penetrate the skin through the layers, the hair follicles and sweat glands. The amount of penetration is affected by the health and condition of the skin. Splits, cuts, tears and irregularities caused by disease or disorder increase the risk of infection.

Protection

The skin acts as a barrier to the body's invasion by micro-organisms like bacteria. The naturally acid pH of the skin's surface inhibits bacterial production. Melanin, the pigment produced by the melanocytes in the basal layer of the epidermis, has a protective function. It helps to protect against ultraviolet light damage to tissues. Sensory nerve endings found at differing levels in the dermis warn of possible trauma and, by reflex action, prevent greater damage to the body.

Elimination

Some toxins are eliminated from the body through the skin via the sweat glands. The toxins normally take the form of waste salts and water.

Sensation

Specialised nerve endings found in the dermis make the body aware of its surroundings. They warn of pain, cold, heat, pressure and touch. Different receptors lie at different levels in the skin. Pain and touch receptors are closer to the surface. All receptors warn of and prevent trauma to the skin and underlying structures.

Vitamin D formation

Vitamin D is essential for the formation and maintenance of bone. Vitamin D production is stimulated by ultraviolet light which converts a fatty substance in the skin, ergosterol, into vitamin D. This circulates in the blood and any excess is stored in the liver. Lack of vitamin D results in rickets in children.

Melanin formation

In the sun, the body makes melanocyte-stimulating hormone (MSH) which causes the melanocytes in the basal layer of the epidermis to produce melanin, a substance which produces a darkening of the skin to protect the underlying structures. The pigment protects the body from harmful effects of the sun's rays since dark colours absorb radiation.

You now know all about the structure and functions of skin. The next section explains the diseases and disorders that can affect this organ.

> ### Did you know?
> The skin is the largest organ in the human body. If you stretched it out flat it would measure from eleven to eighteen square metres in area and total about 12% of the weight of a human.

DISEASES AND DISORDERS

Diseases and disorders of the skin fall into six different categories:
- **Congenital** (exists at birth, may be inherited) e.g. eczema
- **Bacterial** e.g. acne vulgaris
- **Viral** e.g. herpes simplex
- **Fungal** e.g. tinea pedis (Athlete's foot)
- **Pigmentation disorders** e.g. moles and freckles
- **General** e.g. comedones and milia (blackheads and whiteheads).

Congenital
- **Eczema**: found all over the body but most often on the inside of the knee (in the popliteal space) and elbow joints,

on the face, hands and scalp. The skin becomes extremely dry and itchy causing great discomfort. Skin has scaly dry patches with bleeding at points. Not contagious.

- **Psoriasis**: chronic inflammatory skin disease characterised by red patches covered with silvery scales that are constantly shed. Size of scales vary from minute spots to quite large sheets of skin. Points of bleeding may occur beneath scales. Affects whole body or specific areas, like face and scalp. Not infectious.

Bacterial

● **Acne vulgaris**: normally caused by hormonal imbalances which increase sebum production leading to blocked glands and infection. The skin has a shiny, sallow appearance with papules, pustules and comedones. It is prone to open pores. Where pustules have cleared there is often pitting and scarring. The main sites for infection are the face, back, chest and shoulders. Not contagious.

● **Folliculitis**: bacterial infection of the pilo-sebaceous duct (sebaceous gland and hair follicle) causing inflammation. Common in adolescence. Possible link with acne vulgaris.

● **Boils**: a bacterial infection of the skin, causing inflammation around a hair follicle.

● **Impetigo**: a bacterial infection causing thin-roofed blisters which weep and leave a thick, yellow crust. Highly contagious.

● **Acne rosacea**: gives a flushed, reddened appearance. Occurs on the face, this condition can be aggravated by anything causing vasodilation – heat, sunshine, spicy food, alcohol, cold. Affects both men and women especially menopausal women. Not related to acne vulgaris. Not contagious.

Viral

● **Warts**: a small horny tumour found on the skin, often on fingers and thumbs. Caused by viral infection. Highly contagious.
● **Verrucas**: warts found on the feet. Highly contagious.

● **Herpes simplex**: a viral infection commonly known as cold sores; not confined to the mouth, can spread over the face and other parts of the body. Appears as small blisters which if left alone will dry up leaving a crust which falls off. Highly contagious when active.

● **Herpes zoster**: a viral infection commonly known as shingles. Adult form of chicken pox. Usually affects spinal nerves and one side of the thorax. Highly contagious.

Fungal

● **Tinea corporis, pedis**: infections which attach themselves to keratinised structures like the skin. Tinea corporis is commonly known as ringworm and can be found anywhere on the body. Tinea pedis is commonly known as athlete's foot. Highly infectious.

Pigmentation disorders

● **Vitiligo**: a complete loss of colour in well-defined areas of the face and limbs. A form of leucoderma (an abnormal whiteness of the skin due to absence of pigmentation); begins in patches but may converge to form fairly large areas; most obvious in darker skins.

● **Albinism**: complete lack of melanocytes resulting in lack of pigmentation in skin, hair and eyes. Sufferers have poor eyesight and extreme ultraviolet sensitivity. This is an inherited condition.

● **Chloasma**: butterfly mask often caused by pregnancy and the contraceptive pill; a pigmentation condition involving the upper cheeks, nose and occasionally forehead. Discolouration usually disappears spontaneously at the end of the pregnancy.

● **Ephelides**: freckles; small pigmented areas of skin which become more

● Did you know?

The colour of your hair is affected by the amount of melanin in your body. For example, grey hair is caused by a decrease in melanin production. Instead of the pigment (providing colour), there are air bubbles in the hairs and to the naked eye the hair now looks grey.

evident on exposure to sunlight and are found in greatest abundance on the face, arms and legs; fair-skinned individuals suffer most from the condition.

- **Lentigo**: also known as liver spots; dark patches of pigmentation which appear more distinct than freckles and have a slightly raised appearance and more scattered distribution.

- **Moles (papilloma)**: a common occurrence on the face and body and present in several different forms, varying in size, colour and vascular appearance. Flat moles are called sessile whilst those raised above the surface, or attached by a stalk are pedunculated.

- **Naevae**: birth mark; if pigmented may occur on any part of the body and are often found on the neck and face, being sometimes associated with strong hair growth. Vary in size from pinhead to several centimetres and in rare cases may be extremely large. Pigmentation varies from light brown to black. Strawberry naevae (pink or red birth marks) often affect babies, eventually disappearing after a few years.

- **Port wine stain**: a large area of dilated capillaries causing a pink to dark red skin colour which makes it contrast vividly with the surrounding skin. The stain is commonly found on the face.

General

- **Broken capillaries**: dilated capillaries on a fine skin texture often affecting large areas of the face. The skin responds fiercely to stimulation and permanent dilated vessels are apparent, particularly on the upper cheeks and nose. Ruptured blood vessels assume a line-like appearance in surface tissues and can become bulbous and blue in colour due to the congestion in the blood vessels of the area.

- **Crow's feet**: fine lines around the eyes caused by habitual expressions and daily movement, associated with ageing of muscle tissue. Premature formation may be due to eye strain and is often associated with oedema (swelling) around and under the eyes.

- **UV damage**: UV rays stimulate rapid production of basal cells. This causes the stratum corneum to thicken. Over-exposure to UVA may cause premature ageing whereas over-exposure to UVB may cause skin cancer.

- **Urticaria – hives, nettle rash**: often an allergic reaction. Characterised by weals or welts of pinkish colour produced by extreme dilation of capillaries. Very itchy. Can lead to secondary infection by bacteria through scratching.

- **Allergic reaction**: when irritated, the body produces histamine (part of the defence mechanism) in the skin. This can cause red, blotchy patches on skin, watery, stinging eyes, swellings and runny nose. Can be slight or intense, depending on each body's reaction.

- **Comedones**: commonly known as blackheads, these are caused by a build-up of sebaceous secretions which have become trapped in the hair follicles and have subsequently dried out and hardened. The colour comes from oxidation. Common in puberty.

- **Dermatitis**: an allergic inflammation of the skin characterised by erythema – redness of the skin, itching and various skin lesions. Commonly known as contact dermatitis, there are many causes including plants, drugs, clothing, cosmetics and chemicals. Not contagious.

- **Milia**: commonly known as whiteheads, these form when sebum becomes trapped in a blind duct with no surface opening. The condition is most common on dry skin and milia appear on the obicularis oculi muscle area and between the eyebrows. Milia can form after injury, e.g. sunburn on the face or shoulders, and are sometimes widespread.

Skin cancer

There are three types of skin cancer, all caused by excessive exposure to sunlight:

- **Basal cell carcinoma**

Occurs on exposed parts of the skin, especially face, nose, eyelid, cheek.

- **Squamous cell carcinoma**

Squamous cells are those found on the surface of the body, on the top layer of the skin. Squamous cell carcinoma is said to be caused by sunlight, chemicals or physical irritants. It starts very small but grows rapidly, becoming raised.

- **Malignant melanoma**

A malignant tumour of melanocytes. It usually develops in a previously benign mole. The mole has become larger and darker, ulcerated and the tumour eventually spreads.

● SUMMARY

- *Skin is composed of two layers, the epidermis and the dermis*
- *The skin has eight functions: secretion; heat regulation; absorption; protection; elimination; sensation; Vitamin D production; melanin production.*
- *The skin is affected by six different types of disease: congenital; bacterial; viral; fungal; pigmentation disorders and skin cancers.*

The Skeletal System

The skeleton or skeletal system consists of the bones and the joints of the body.

In Brief

The skeleton is a hard framework of 206 bones that supports and protects the muscles and organs of the human body. It is divided into two parts:

- **the axial skeleton**: this supports the head, neck and trunk (also known as torso). It consists of the skull, the vertebral column, the ribs and the sternum
- **the appendicular skeleton**: this supports the appendages or limbs and attaches them to the rest of the body. It consists of the shoulder girdle, the upper limbs, the pelvic girdle and the lower limbs.

THE SKELETON: ANTERIOR VIEW

Learning objectives

The target knowledge of this chapter is:
- the structure of the skeleton including names and position of all bones
- the function of the skeleton
- the types of bone and bone tissue
- types of deformity, fracture and disease affecting the skeleton.

THE SKELETAL SYSTEM

Structure

The skeleton is made up of bones. There are 206 individual bones in the human body and five different types, defined according to their shape:

- **long bones**: the body's levers, they allow movement, particularly in the limbs e.g. the femur (thigh bone), tibia and fibula (lower leg bones), clavicle (collar bone), humerus (upper arm bone), the radius and the ulna (lower arm), metacarpals (hand bones), metatarsals (foot bones) and phalanges (finger and toe bones).
- **short bones**: strong and compact bones, usually grouped in parts of the body where little movement is required e.g. tarsals (ankle bones) and carpals (wrist bones).
- **flat bones**: protective bones with broad flat surfaces for muscle attachment e.g. occipital, parietal, frontal, nasal, vomer, lacrimal (all of these are in the skull), scapula (shoulder bone), innominate bones (pelvis), sternum (breastbone), ribs.
- **irregular bones**: bones that do not fit into the above categories and have different characteristics e.g. vertebrae, including the sacrum and coccyx (backbone), maxilla, mandible, ethmoid, palatine, sphenoid, zygomatic (cheek) and temporal (all bones of the face and head).
- **sesamoid bones**: bones within tendons. There are only two sesamoid bones in the human body, the kneecap, or patella, and the hyoid (base of the tongue).

Functions

- supports the body: all body tissues (apart from cartilage and bone) are soft so without the skeleton the body would be jelly-like and could not stand up. The bones and their arrangement give the body its shape.
- allows and enables movement
- protects delicate body organs e.g. the cranium, or skull, is a hard shell surrounding the soft brain and the thoracic cage (ribs and sternum) covers the heart and lungs
- forms blood cells (in the red bone marrow)
- forms joints which are essential for the movement of the body
- provides attachment for muscles which move the joints: muscles are attached to bones and pull them into different positions, thus moving the body
- provides a store of calcium salts and phosphorus.

The Skeleton

An easy way to remember the differences between the axial and appendicular parts of the skeleton is to think of axes (i.e. the centre) versus appendage (i.e. the added bits). The centre is the head, neck and torso, the added bits are the arms and legs and the bones that attach them to the body.

What are bones made of?

Bones are living tissue made from special cells called osteoblasts. The tissue varies considerably in density and compactness: the closer to the surface of the bone the more compact it is. Many bones have a central cavity containing marrow, a tissue which is the source of most of the cells of the blood and is also a site for the storage of fats. There are two main types of bone tissue:

● **compact**: to the naked eye this looks like a solid structure but under a microscope it looks like honeycomb, i.e. full of holes. Haversian canals (see below) are passageways containing blood vessels, lymph capillaries and nerves which run through the tissue. Compact bone is found on the outside of most bones and in the shaft of long bones.

● **cancellous**: this type of bone looks like a sponge and it is found at the ends of long bones and in irregular, flat and sesamoid bones. Bone marrow only exists in cancellous bone.

All bones have both types of tissue. The amount of each depends on the type of bone.

What are Haversian canals?

Haversian canals run lengthways through compact bone and contain blood and lymph capillaries and nerves. The larger the canal the less dense and compact the bones.

You now know what a skeleton is, what types of bone make a skeleton, what a bone is and what bones are made of. The following series of detailed diagrams illustrate and name the major bones in the skeleton starting with the axial section.

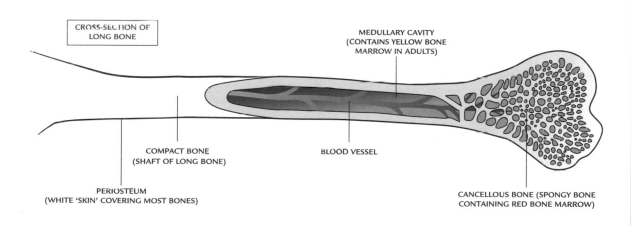

CROSS-SECTION OF LONG BONE

MEDULLARY CAVITY (CONTAINS YELLOW BONE MARROW IN ADULTS)

COMPACT BONE (SHAFT OF LONG BONE)

BLOOD VESSEL

PERIOSTEUM (WHITE 'SKIN' COVERING MOST BONES)

CANCELLOUS BONE (SPONGY BONE CONTAINING RED BONE MARROW)

CANCELLOUS BONE SEEN UNDER MICROSCOPE

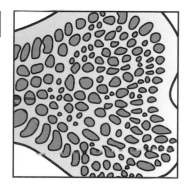

Section 1: the axial skeleton

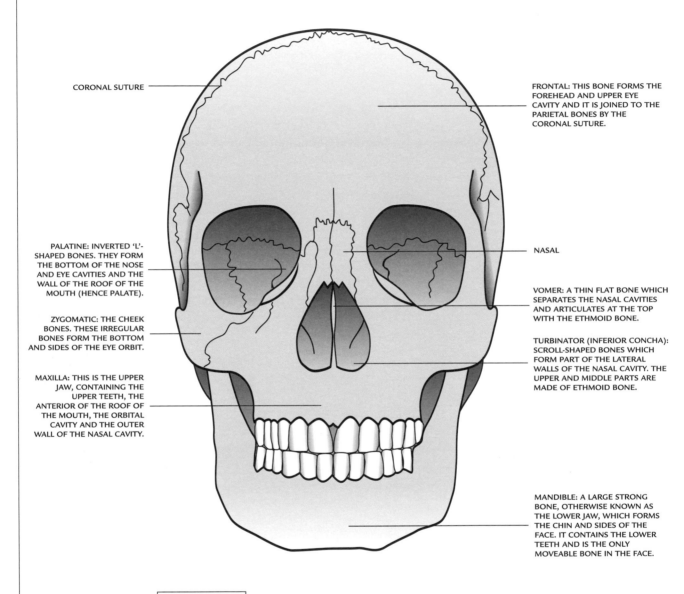

SKULL: ANTERIOR VIEW

CORONAL SUTURE

FRONTAL: THIS BONE FORMS THE FOREHEAD AND UPPER EYE CAVITY AND IT IS JOINED TO THE PARIETAL BONES BY THE CORONAL SUTURE.

PALATINE: INVERTED 'L'-SHAPED BONES. THEY FORM THE BOTTOM OF THE NOSE AND EYE CAVITIES AND THE WALL OF THE ROOF OF THE MOUTH (HENCE PALATE).

NASAL

VOMER: A THIN FLAT BONE WHICH SEPARATES THE NASAL CAVITIES AND ARTICULATES AT THE TOP WITH THE ETHMOID BONE.

ZYGOMATIC: THE CHEEK BONES. THESE IRREGULAR BONES FORM THE BOTTOM AND SIDES OF THE EYE ORBIT.

TURBINATOR (INFERIOR CONCHA): SCROLL-SHAPED BONES WHICH FORM PART OF THE LATERAL WALLS OF THE NASAL CAVITY. THE UPPER AND MIDDLE PARTS ARE MADE OF ETHMOID BONE.

MAXILLA: THIS IS THE UPPER JAW, CONTAINING THE UPPER TEETH, THE ANTERIOR OF THE ROOF OF THE MOUTH, THE ORBITAL CAVITY AND THE OUTER WALL OF THE NASAL CAVITY.

MANDIBLE: A LARGE STRONG BONE, OTHERWISE KNOWN AS THE LOWER JAW, WHICH FORMS THE CHIN AND SIDES OF THE FACE. IT CONTAINS THE LOWER TEETH AND IS THE ONLY MOVEABLE BONE IN THE FACE.

BONES OF THE FACE

● The axial skeleton includes:

Skull: *cranium eight bones; face 14 bones hyoid: one bone*
Vertebral column: *33 vertebrae, some fused, so 26 bones in total*
Sternum: *three bones*
Ribs: *12 pairs (24 bones)*

SKULL: SIDE VIEW

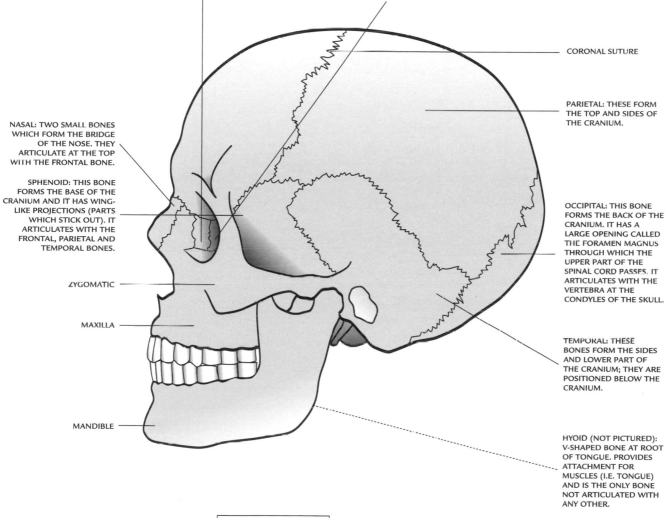

LACRIMAL: VERY SMALL BONES POSITIONED BEHIND AND LATERAL TO THE NASAL BONES. THEY ARE IN THE EYE SOCKET AND CONTAIN FORAMINA FOR THE PASSAGE OF THE NASOLACRIMAL DUCT (TEAR DUCT) HENCE THEIR NAME.

ETHMOID: THE ETHMOID IS POSITIONED BELOW THE FRONTAL BONE AND IN FRONT OF THE SPHENOID BONE. IT HELPS TO FORM THE ORBITAL CAVITY (SPACE FOR THE EYES) AND THE NASAL CAVITY (SPACE FOR THE NOSE).

CORONAL SUTURE

PARIETAL: THESE FORM THE TOP AND SIDES OF THE CRANIUM.

NASAL: TWO SMALL BONES WHICH FORM THE BRIDGE OF THE NOSE. THEY ARTICULATE AT THE TOP WITH THE FRONTAL BONE.

SPHENOID: THIS BONE FORMS THE BASE OF THE CRANIUM AND IT HAS WING-LIKE PROJECTIONS (PARTS WHICH STICK OUT). IT ARTICULATES WITH THE FRONTAL, PARIETAL AND TEMPORAL BONES.

OCCIPITAL: THIS BONE FORMS THE BACK OF THE CRANIUM. IT HAS A LARGE OPENING CALLED THE FORAMEN MAGNUS THROUGH WHICH THE UPPER PART OF THE SPINAL CORD PASSES. IT ARTICULATES WITH THE VERTEBRA AT THE CONDYLES OF THE SKULL.

ZYGOMATIC

MAXILLA

TEMPORAL: THESE BONES FORM THE SIDES AND LOWER PART OF THE CRANIUM; THEY ARE POSITIONED BELOW THE CRANIUM.

MANDIBLE

HYOID (NOT PICTURED): V-SHAPED BONE AT ROOT OF TONGUE. PROVIDES ATTACHMENT FOR MUSCLES (I.E. TONGUE) AND IS THE ONLY BONE NOT ARTICULATED WITH ANY OTHER.

BONES OF THE CRANIUM

THE SKELETAL SYSTEM

Did you know?

Laughing and coughing put more pressure on the spine than walking or standing.

CERVICAL
(7 BONES)
THORACIC
(12 BONES)
INTERVERTEBRAL DISCS
LUMBAR
(5 BONES)
THE SACRAL (FIVE BONES) AND COCCYGEAL (FOUR BONES) VERTEBRAE ARE KNOWN AS FALSE OR FIXED VERTEBRAE BECAUSE, UNLIKE TRUE VERTEBRAE, THEY CANNOT MOVE INDEPENDENTLY AND THERE IS NO MOVEMENT BETWEEN THEM. HOWEVER, THE COCCYX DOES MOVE IN RELATION TO THE SACRUM.
THE FIRST THREE TYPES OF VERTEBRAE ARE KNOWN AS TRUE VERTEBRAE BECAUSE THEY MOVE. THEY ARE SEPARATED BY INTERVERTEBRAL DISCS, PADS OF FIBROCARTILAGE, WHICH HAVE SHOCK-ABSORBING FUNCTIONS.

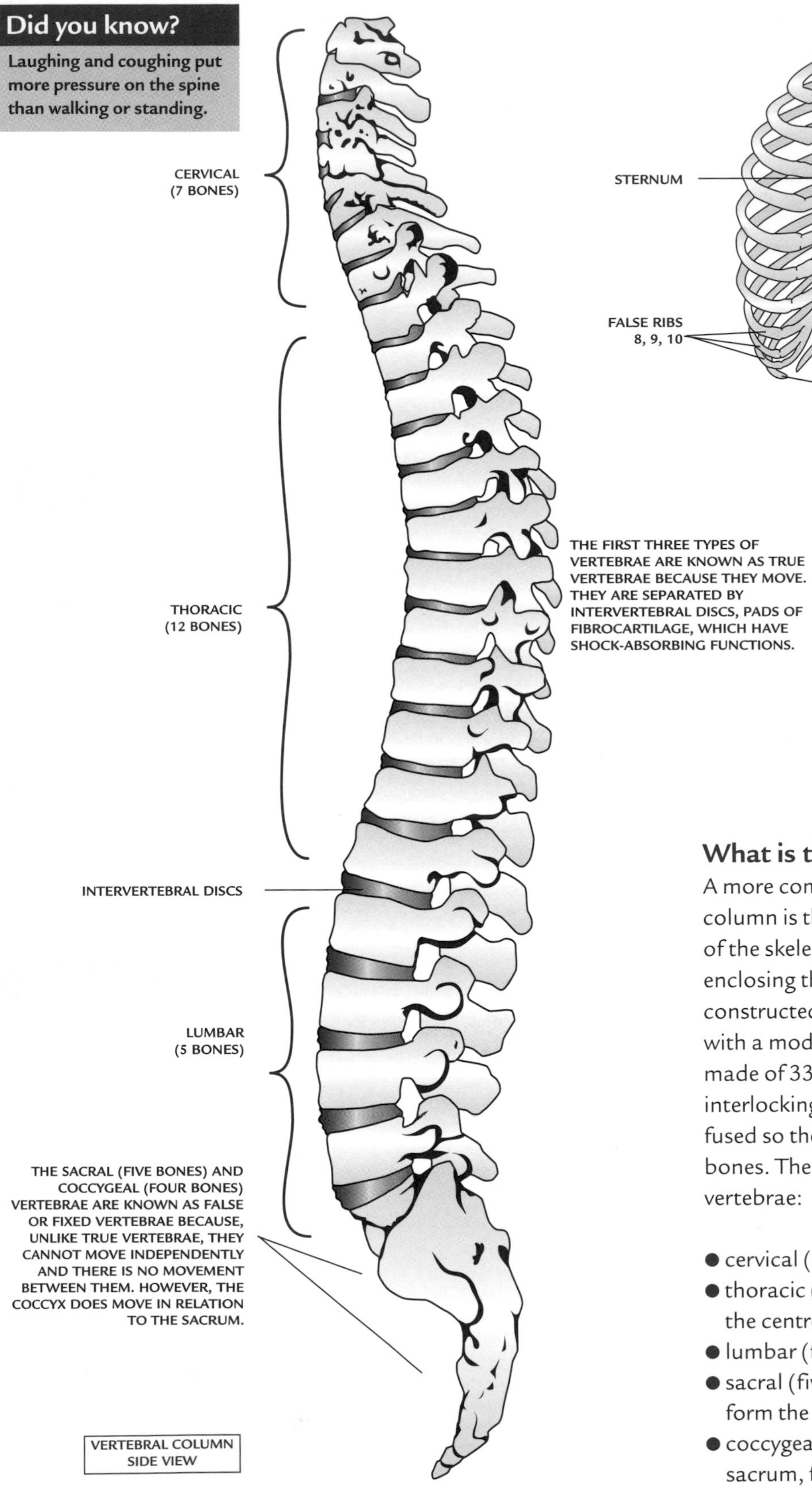

VERTEBRAL COLUMN
SIDE VIEW

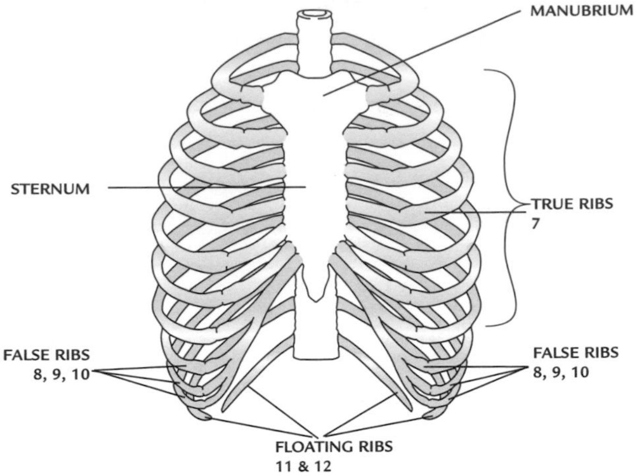

MANUBRIUM
STERNUM
TRUE RIBS
7
FALSE RIBS
8, 9, 10
FALSE RIBS
8, 9, 10
FLOATING RIBS
11 & 12

THORACIC CAGE
ANTERIOR VIEW

What is the vertebral column?

A more common name for the vertebral column is the spine. It is the central part of the skeleton, supporting the head and enclosing the spinal cord and it is constructed to combine great strength with a moderate degree of mobility. It is made of 33 vertebrae – irregular, interlocking bones. Some of these are fused so there are only 26 individual bones. There are five different types of vertebrae:

- cervical (seven bones in the neck)
- thoracic (12 bones carrying the ribs in the centre of the body)
- lumbar (five bones in the lower back)
- sacral (five bones in the pelvis, fused to form the sacrum)
- coccygeal (four bones below the sacrum, forming the coccyx).

You now know the positions and names of all the major bones in the axial skeleton. The next section covers the appendicular skeleton, the shoulder and pelvic girdles, arms and legs.

Section 2: the appendicular skeleton

The appendicular skeleton includes:

Shoulder girdle: two scapulae and two clavicles

Arm: one humerus, one ulna, one radius (each arm)

Wrist: eight carpal bones (each wrist)

Hand: five metacarpal bones (each palm of hand)

Fingers: 14 phalanges in each hand, two in a thumb and three each in the other fingers

Pelvic girdle: two innominate bones (each one including an ilium, ischium and pubis)

Leg: one femur, one tibia, one fibula and one patella (each leg)

Ankle and foot: seven tarsals and five metatarsals (each foot)

Toes: 14 phalanges in each foot, two in a big toe and three each in the other toes.

The shoulder girdle

The shoulder girdle consists of two scapulae (shoulder blades) and two clavicles (collar bones). These four bones form an incomplete ring, articulating with the manubrium – the flat part at the top of the sternum (breast bone) – at the front, hence the name girdle.

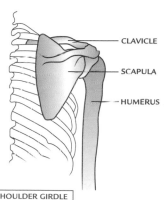

SHOULDER GIRDLE
(ANTERIOR VIEW)

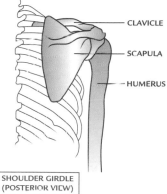

SHOULDER GIRDLE
(POSTERIOR VIEW)

The pelvic girdle

The pelvic girdle is formed by two large innominate bones which meet in front at the symphysis pubis and articulate with the sacrum in the back to form a ring of bone. The innominate bones, with the sacrum and coccyx, form the pelvis which surrounds the pelvic cavity. The pelvis of the female is wider and shallower than that of the male. Each innominate bone is formed by the fusion of three parts – an ilium, an ischium and a pubis. At the junction of these is a socket for the head of the femur.

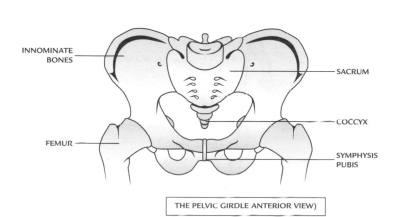

THE PELVIC GIRDLE ANTERIOR VIEW)

JOINTS

What are joints?

Joints are the body's hinges. There are three types:

- Fixed, or fibrous joints
- Slightly moveable, or cartilaginous joints
- Freely movable, or synovial joints.

Fixed, or fibrous joints

Chararacteristics: no movement
Structure: fibrous tissue between the ends of the bones e.g. sutures in the skull, innominate (pelvic girdle) bones.

Slightly moveable, or cartilaginous joints

Characteristics: slightly moveable, moves by compression of the cartilage
Structure: pad of white fibrocartilage between the bones, e.g. spine.

Freely moveable, or synovial joints

Five different types: ball and socket; hinge; gliding; pivot; saddle.

Fixed or fibrous

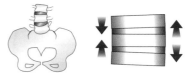

Slightly moveable, or cartilaginous joints

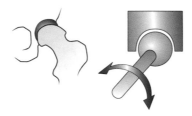

Ball and socket: most moveable of all joints. Allow flexion, extension, adduction, abduction, rotation and circumduction e.g. shoulder and hip joints.

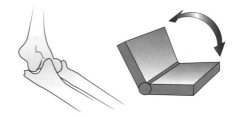

Hinge: movement in one direction (plane) only. Movements are flexion and extension e.g. elbow, knee, ankle, joints between phalanges of fingers and toes.

Gliding joints: the bones glide over each other; the least moveable of joints e.g. between tarsals and carpals.

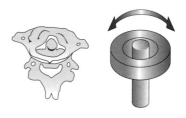

Pivot joints: movement around one axis only and a rotary movement e.g. first two cervical vertebrae (atlas and axis) which allow the head to rotate and proximal ends of radius and ulna.

Saddle joints: movement around two axes (like ball and socket) allowing flexion, extension, adduction, abduction, circumduction. Found only between the phalanges of the thumb and its metacarpal.

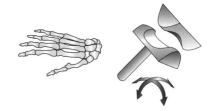

You now know what joints are and how they work. The final section explains postural deformities, fractures and certain bone diseases.

What are postural deformities?

The spine has two natural curves: an inward curve in the lower back (lumbar area: put your hand there and try it) and a slight outward curve in the upper back (the thoracic area). In certain cases, the spine's natural curves become exaggerated, causing unnatural curves, or postural deformities. There are three causes for these:

- **congenital**: those which are present at birth or are hereditary.
- **environmental**: sitting and standing incorrectly can cause long-term damage to the spine. Many people in sedentary work are affected by these causes.
- **traumatic**: caused by accidents.

What do postural deformities look like?

Kyphosis: an exaggerated outward curvature of the spine (Quasimodo, the central character of Victor Hugo's novel, *The Hunchback of Notre Dame*, is probably the most famous of all real or fictional sufferers of kyphosis)

Scoliosis: a sideways curvature of the spine

Lordosis: an exaggerated inward curvature of the spine.

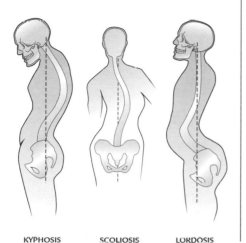

KYPHOSIS   SCOLIOSIS   LORDOSIS

What is a fracture?

A fracture is the breakage of a bone due either to injury or disease. There are six different types:

- **simple**: a bone has broken in one place and not damaged the tissue around it
- **compound:** (sometimes called open) a fracture in which the broken bone pierces the skin and/or communicates with the surface of the skin through an open wound
- **comminuted**: a bone broken in several places
- **greenstick**: more common in soft and flexible bones, especially children's, this is an incomplete fracture of a long bone
- **impacted**: a bone which has been broken and then one end is driven into the other (like one car shunting into the back of another)
- **complicated** (not pictured): broken bone which damages tissue and/or organs around it.

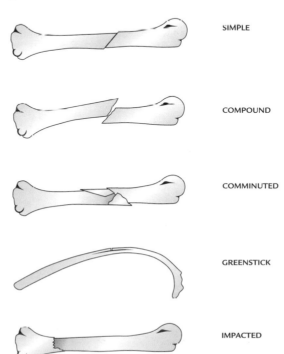

SIMPLE

COMPOUND

COMMINUTED

GREENSTICK

IMPACTED

DISEASES AND DISORDERS

Arthritis

Arthritis is an inflammation of the joints. Mono-articular arthritis is an inflammation of one joint and poly-arthritis is an inflammation of many. It can be acute or chronic:

- **acute**: symptoms are heat, redness, and visible inflammation of the affected joints accompanied by severe pain.
- **chronic**: involves loss of cartilage, deposition of bone tissue around the joint margins and lesser degrees of pain and inflammation.

Gout

A form of arthritis that can occur in any part of the body but often affects the big toe; more common in men than women.
Cause: deposition of uric acid crystals within the joint capsule and cartilage.
Effect: attacks of acute gouty arthritis, chronic destruction of joints.

Osteo-arthritis (also known as degenerative)

Cause: may be injury of the joint or, if widespread, may be associated with the ageing process.
Effect: chronic arthritis of degenerative type – cartilage of joint breaks down; usually affects weight-bearing joints like knees, feet and back.

Rheumatoid arthritis (type of poly-arthritis)

Cause: an auto immune disease that attacks the synovial membranes and goes on to degrade and malform the articular surfaces of the bones.

Effect: acute and chronic phases with varying degrees of damage and deformity.

Ankylosing spondylitis: type of arthritis with acute and chronic phases which results in fusion of the joints of the spine causing severe deformity and immobility.

Osteoporosis

(also known as brittle bone disease)
Cause: calcium deficiency; accelerated bone loss especially in post-menopausal women.
Effect: porosity and brittleness of bones.

Slipped disc

Cause: the weakening or tearing of one of the intervertebral discs.
Effect: disc bulges or sticks out and this may press on the spinal nerve causing pain.

Stress

Stress is any factor which affects mental or physical health. When stressed, muscle tension increases and this causes poor posture (for example hunched shoulders or a clenched jaw), stiff joints and problems with the spinal vertebrae.

Interrelationships

Skeletal system links to:
Muscular: muscles always cross joints and thus rely on the framework of the skeleton for leverage and movement.
Circulatory: erythrocytes are produced in the bone marrow of long bones.
Nervous: muscles require a nerve impulse to contract which produces movement in the skeleton.
Digestive: breaks down foodstuffs and works with the circulatory system to transport nutrients to bone tissues.
Urinary: a hormone produced by the kidneys helps to stimulate the production of bone marrow in long bones.

SUMMARY

- *The skeleton is composed of bones and joints which form the axial (central head, neck and torso) skeleton and the appendicular (appendages – arms and legs) skeleton.*
- *It protects and supports the body, allows movement, produces blood cells (in red bone marrow), stores calcium and provides attachment for muscles.*
- *The skeleton is susceptible to breakage (fractures), and postural deformities caused by congenital or environmental factors.*

The Muscular System

Muscles are the body's movers and shakers. These tissues are attached to other parts of the body and when they relax and contract they enable movement.

In Brief

The muscular system comprises the muscles of the body and their attachments — tendons and fascia. When muscle fibres contract the muscles change shape and move whichever part of the body they are attached to. This can be a voluntary (conscious) movement such as lifting an arm or an involuntary movement such as vasoconstriction of the tiny muscles in the skin.

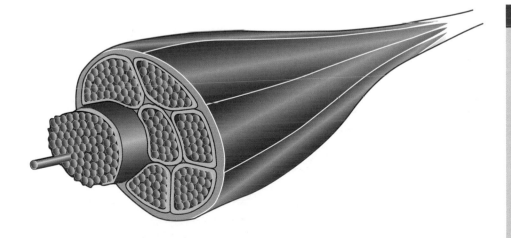

CROSS-SECTION OF A MUSCLE

Learning objectives

The target knowledge of this chapter is:
- the different types of muscular tissue and their functions
- the different types of muscular attachment
- the different actions performed by muscles
- how muscles contract
- how lactic acid is formed and how it affects muscles
- the position and action of all the major muscles in the body
- the diseases and disorders of the muscular system.

THE MUSCULAR SYSTEM

STRUCTURE

What is a muscle?

A muscle is a group of specialised, elastic tissues. More of the human body is made of muscle than any other tissue: 23% of a woman's body weight and about 40% of a man's.

Structure: muscle tissue is bound together in bundles and contained in a sheath (sometimes called a fascia), the end of which extends to form a tendon that attaches the muscle to other parts of the body. Muscle is 75% water, 20% proteins, 5% fats, mineral salts and glycogen.

Function: a muscle's function is to contract and by doing so start a movement in the surrounding structures (the tendons, ligaments and eventually bones). The muscle contracts in reaction to a nerve stimulus sent by the brain through a motor nerve. The muscle then shortens becoming fatter at the centre.

Summary of muscular functions

1. *contract and thereby produce movement e.g. to move joints*
2. *stabilise joints*
3. *maintain postural tone*
4. *aid in temperature control e.g. shivering and dilation of capillaries (see Skin).*

What does muscle look like?

There are three types of muscular tissue, each with a different structure.

Voluntary muscle

(sometimes called skeletal or striated muscle)

Function: these are the muscles which we consciously control e.g. our arms and legs. If we want to walk we do so.

Structure: voluntary muscle has cylindrical cells which make up fibres. Each fibre has several nuclei (multi-nucleated cells) and is surrounded by a sheath (sarcolemma). The muscle fibres form bundles and they all run in the same direction. Under a microscope voluntary muscle looks stripy. The stripes or striations are made of proteins (actin and myosin filaments) which run across the muscle fibres in transverse bands; they are alternately light and dark and they give voluntary muscle its other name: striated muscle. When the muscle contracts the actin filaments slide between the myosin filaments which causes a shortening and thickening of the fibres.

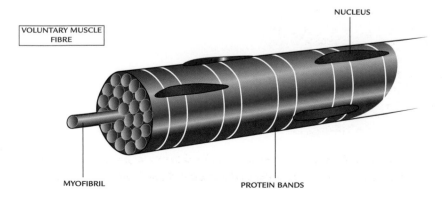

VOLUNTARY MUSCLE FIBRE

NUCLEUS

MYOFIBRIL

PROTEIN BANDS

Involuntary muscle
(sometimes called smooth muscle)

Function: these are the muscles we do not consciously control e.g. those that are found in the walls of blood and lymphatic vessels, in respiratory, digestive and genito-urinary systems. These muscles work automatically whether we want them to or not!

Structure: involuntary muscles have spindle-shaped cells with no distinct membrane and only one nucleus. Bundles of the fibres form the muscle we see with the naked eye. Under a microscope they have no stripes which is why they are also known as smooth muscles.

Cardiac muscle
Function: to power the pump action of the heart.

Structure: cardiac muscle only exists in the heart; it is involuntary muscle tissue but its fibres are striated and each cell has one nucleus so, in structure, it resembles voluntary muscle. Each cell or fibre has a nucleus.

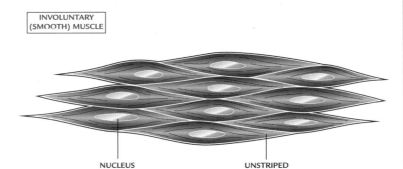

INVOLUNTARY (SMOOTH) MUSCLE

NUCLEUS

UNSTRIPED MUSCLE CELL

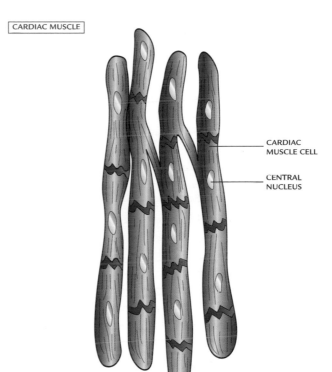

CARDIAC MUSCLE

CARDIAC MUSCLE CELL

CENTRAL NUCLEUS

Smallest, largest and strongest

- *The smallest skeletal muscle (i.e. a muscle attached to a bone) is the stapedius in the ear. It activates the stapes, the stirrup-shaped bone in the middle ear which sends vibrations from the eardrum to the inner ear.*
- *The largest muscle in the body is the latissimus dorsi, the flat back muscle which covers the central and lower back.*
- *The strongest muscle in the body is the gluteus maximus which forms the main bulk of the buttock. This muscle is responsible for lifting the torso after bending down or leaning over.*

You now know what a muscle is and the structure and function of the three types of muscular tissue. The following section explains how muscles work and the names of the different muscle parts.

FUNCTION

Human babies, unlike some other mammals, are not born knowing how to control the voluntary muscles that help us stand and move. They learn to control and co-ordinate muscles in the following order: first the head, then the neck, the shoulders and arms, and then the lower parts of the body. When a baby finally learns to stand and walk, it has mastered all the muscles of movement because the last ones in the learning process are the pelvis and legs.

● **Did you know?**

The adductor muscles, which take the limb towards the medial line, are also found in bivalve seashells — those with two hinged parts like clams, oysters, mussels and cockles. The muscle closes the shell.

How do muscles work?

By contraction: the fibres become shorter and thicker and the parts attached to the fibres (periosteum, bone, tendons and fascia) are pulled by the contraction and move. When a muscle fibre contracts it follows the 'all or nothing' law i.e. it contracts completely or not at all. Involuntary muscle and cardiac muscle contract independently of our conscious will. Voluntary muscles, however, move because we want them to e.g. when we walk, lift our arm, hand or foot or bend down. There are two types of contraction:
● **isometric**: the muscle contracts but produces no movement
● **isotonic**: the muscle contracts and moves with the tension remaining unaltered within the muscle.

How does movement happen?

In skeletal muscle (those attached to bones) a muscle needs to pass over a joint to create movement. Muscle contraction pulls one bone towards another and thus moves the limb. Muscles never work alone: any movement results from the actions of several muscles. In general, muscles work in pairs. Each pair contains an antagonist (the opposing, relaxing muscle) and an agonist (the contracting muscle). The agonist and the antagonist must contract and relax equally to ensure a smooth and not jerky movement.

How does a muscle know when to contract?

The stimulus to contract comes from the nervous system through the nerves. Motor nerves enter the muscles and break into many nerve endings, each one stimulating a single muscle fibre.

Where does a muscle get energy from?

In order for contraction (and therefore movement) to take place, there must be an adequate blood supply to provide oxygen and nutrients and to remove waste products from energy production. Muscles receive their nutrients and oxygen from the arterial capillaries. This is converted into energy by chemical changes. The nutrients and oxygen are used up by the muscle and the waste product, lactic acid, is then excreted into the venous blood stream.

A muscle's ability to contract is affected by the following factors:
● energy available
● strength of the stimulus from the nerve
● time muscle has been contracting
● adequate blood supply bringing enough oxygen and nutrients
● strength of inhibitory nerve supply
● temperature of muscle (warmth increases response)
● presence of waste products like lactic acid.

Different stages of contraction

Tone: slight degree of contraction by some fibres as others are relaxing. In normal healthy muscles there will always be a few muscle fibres contracting at any one time, even during sleep. This action gives normal posture to the body.

Relaxation: a lessening of tension, so a reduction in the number of fibres contracting at any one time. Muscle tension can be affected by conscious effort and thought and relaxation can be taught.

Problems with over-contraction

Muscle tension: this is over-stimulation of muscle fibres. More fibres contract than are necessary to maintain postural tone.

Muscle fatigue: when stimulated a muscle will need oxygen and fuel for its energy. This fuel is mainly glucose, stored in the muscle as glycogen and fats and transported by the blood. The muscle burns the glucose and fats by combining them with oxygen from the blood. Muscles that are repeatedly contracting and relaxing need a lot of energy and a lot of oxygen to produce that energy. That is why strenuous exercise causes rapid breathing and makes the exerciser out of breath.

If a muscle continues to contract without enough rest (e.g. if someone does too much exercise without breaks), the muscle will run out of oxygen and a by-product of this deficiency, lactic acid, will build up. This acid causes a burning sensation in the muscle, the muscle begins to quiver and soon stops contracting. The exerciser will feel stiffness and pain in the affected muscle. The muscle will not work properly until it can remove the lactic acid. It will need a fresh supply of oxygen for this. The exerciser will thus have to slow down.

Terms of description for muscles

- **attachment**: muscles can be attached by muscle fibres, tendons or other fibrous bands to each other, or to bones, skin, cartilage or ligaments.
- **belly**: thickest part or main body of muscle; usually the middle part away from insertion and origin.
- **insertion**: the moving end of the muscle, the point to which the force of the muscle is directed.
- **origin**: the fixed end of a muscle. This end of the muscle barely moves during muscle action. N.B. A muscle always works from its insertion towards its origin.

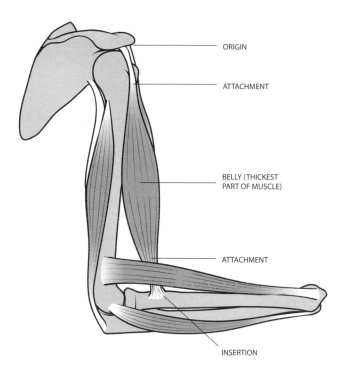

ORIGIN

ATTACHMENT

BELLY (THICKEST PART OF MUSCLE)

ATTACHMENT

INSERTION

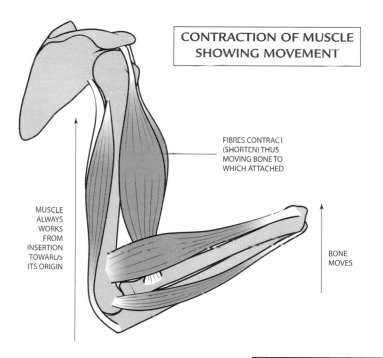

CONTRACTION OF MUSCLE SHOWING MOVEMENT

FIBRES CONTRACT (SHORTEN) THUS MOVING BONE TO WHICH ATTACHED

MUSCLE ALWAYS WORKS FROM INSERTION TOWARDS ITS ORIGIN

BONE MOVES

You now know what muscles are and how they work. The following section explains how muscles fit into the rest of the body and details the movements (actions) and positions of all the main muscles in the human body.

Did you know?

That shivering is caused by muscle contraction? When you're cold your body starts producing body heat by making muscles contract and relax quicker than usual. This is shivering.

HOW ARE MUSCLES ATTACHED TO THE REST OF THE BODY?

Muscles are attached by tendons and the fascia.

Tendon

Structure: white fibrous cords (an extension of the fascia) with no elasticity which are of different lengths and thickness and are very strong. They have few, if any, blood vessels or nerves.

Function: it connects muscle to bone.

Fascia

Structure: white, fibrous connective tissue. It is found in all parts of the body, in different lengths and thicknesses.

Function:

● superficial fascia – beneath the skin; found over almost the whole surface of the body; facilitates the movement of the skin; serves as a medium for the passage of nerves and blood vessels; helps retain body warmth; connects skin with deep fascia.

● deep fascia – dense, inelastic, stiff membrane which forms a sheath (covering) for muscles and broad surfaces for attachment. Made of shiny tendinous fibres it is thicker in unprotected areas and assists muscle action through tension and pressure.

Do all muscles work in the same way?

All muscles work by contraction but each muscle performs a specific action (type of movement) in order to move the body. There are several different actions:

Flexion: bend or flex a limb inwards

Extension: bend or extend a limb outwards

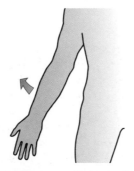

Abduction: move a limb away from the midline

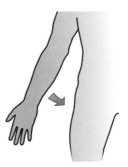

Adduction: move a limb towards the midline

Inversion: turning towards centre e.g. sole of foot

Rotation: rotate head at neck

Eversion: turning outwards away from centre e.g. sole of foot

Supination: turn a limb to face upwards

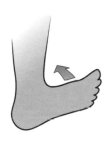

Dorsiflexion: flexing/bending foot up (with toe up, heel down)

Pronation: turn a limb to face downwards

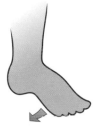

Plantarflexion: flexing/bending foot down towards the ground (with toe down, heel up) e.g. as in walking

Did you know?

The advent of more and more jobs involving the use of computers has resulted in new diseases caused by constant keyboard work. These are known as 'repetitive- strain injuries' or RSIs. The most common repetitive strain injury is 'carpal-tunnel syndrome'. It has been called the 'secretary's disease' but it can affect anyone whose job requires lots of wrist flexion (hence 'carpal' bones of the wrist) or prolonged finger extension. There are different symptoms including wrist pain, swelling and numbness or 'pins-and-needles' in the index and middle fingers.

THE MUSCULAR SYSTEM

The principal muscles of the body

There are thousands of muscles in the body. The following series of diagrams show the principal muscles of the body, detailing their position and their action.

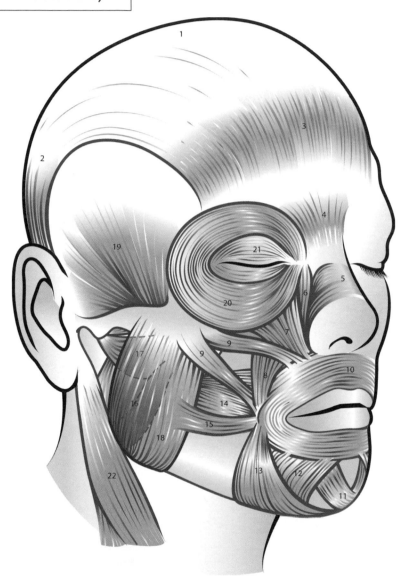

MUSCLES OF THE FACE
(ANTERIOR VIEW)

KEY: P: POSITION   A: ACTION

1. OCCIPITOFRONTALIS
P: THE OCCIPITALIS AND FRONTALIS ARE COLLECTIVELY
   KNOWN AS OCCIPITOFRONTALIS
A: LIFTS EYEBROWS AND WRINKLES SKIN OF FOREHEAD;
   CREATES LOOKS OF SURPRISE AND HORROR

2. OCCIPITALIS
P: FIBROUS SHEET OVER OCCIPITAL BONE
A: MOVES SCALP BACKWARDS

3. FRONTALIS
P: FIBROUS SHEET OVER FRONTAL AND PARIETAL BONES
A: MOVES SCALP FORWARDS

4. PROCERUS NASI
P: CONTINUATION OF FRONTALIS DOWN MIDLINE OF NOSE
   BETWEEN EYEBROWS
A: WRINKLES AT BRIDGE OF NOSE (DISGUSTED EXPRESSION)

5. NASALIS
P: SIDES OF THE NOSE
A: COMPRESSES AND DILATES NASAL OPENING (PRODUCES
   ANNOYED EXPRESSION AND SNIFFING)

KEY: P: POSITION   A: ACTION

6/7. LEVATOR LABII SUPERIORIS
P: THIN BAND OF MUSCLE FROM EYE TO MOUTH
A: LIFTS UPPER LIP; PRODUCES CHEERFUL EXPRESSION

8. LEVATOR ANGULI ORIS
P: THIN BAND OF MUSCLE BELOW LEVATOR LABII SUPERIORIS
A: RAISES CORNER OF MOUTH; PRODUCES CHEERFUL EXPRESSION

9. ZYGOMATICUS
P: THIN MUSCLE ANGLED ACROSS FACE SUPERFICIAL TO MASSETER
A: MOVES ANGLE OF MOUTH UP, BACK AND OUT (SMILING)

10. ORBICULARIS ORIS
P: SPHINCTER MUSCLE AROUND MOUTH
A: PURSES LIPS

11. MENTALIS
P: ABOVE MENTAL TUBEROSITY ON CHIN
A: LIFTS SKIN ON CHIN AND TURNS LOWER LIP OUTWARDS

12. DEPRESSOR LABII INFERIORIS
P: MID-LINE OF CHIN TO LOWER LIP
A: PULLS LOWER LIP STRAIGHT DOWN

13. DEPRESSOR ANGULI ORIS
P: FROM MODIOLUS TO MANDIBLE
A: PULLS DOWN CORNERS OF MOUTH

14. BUCCINATOR
P: BROAD THIN MUSCLE DEEP TO MASSETER
A: COMPRESSES CHEEK AGAINST TEETH TO MAINTAIN TENSION; AIDS IN MASTICATION

15. RISORIUS
P: BETWEEN MASSETER AND CORNER OF MOUTH
A: RETRACTS ANGLE OF MOUTH AND LIFTS UPPER LIP (PRODUCES GRINNING EXPRESSION)

16. MEDIAL PTERYGOID
P: INNER SURFACE OF MANDIBLE
A: RAISES THE MANDIBLE

17. LATERAL PTERYGOID
P: BEHIND THE ZYGOMATIC ARCH (CHEEK BONE)
A: PUSHES MANDIBLE OUT AND OPENS MOUTH

18. MASSETER
P: FROM ZYGOMATIC ARCH TO MANDIBLE
A: RAISES LOWER JAW; CHIEF MUSCLE OF MASTICATION

19. TEMPORALIS
P: FROM TEMPORAL BONE TO MANDIBLE
A: RAISES AND RETRACTS LOWER JAW

20. ORBICULARIS OCULI
P: SPHINCTER MUSCLE AROUND EYE
A: CLOSES EYELID

21. LEVATOR PALPEBRAE
P: UPPER EYELID
A: OPENS UPPER EYELID

22. STERNOCLEIDOMASTOID
P: ROPE-LIKE MUSCLE RUNNING AT AN ANGLE UP SIDES OF NECK
A: FLEXES HEAD AND TURNS FROM SIDE TO SIDE

MUSCLES OF THE HEAD AND NECK (SIDE VIEW)

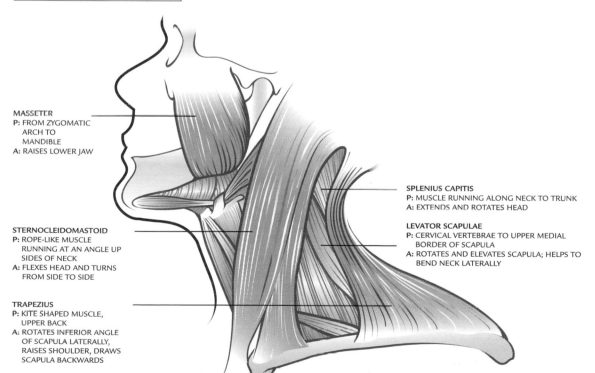

MASSETER
P: FROM ZYGOMATIC ARCH TO MANDIBLE
A: RAISES LOWER JAW

STERNOCLEIDOMASTOID
P: ROPE-LIKE MUSCLE RUNNING AT AN ANGLE UP SIDES OF NECK
A: FLEXES HEAD AND TURNS FROM SIDE TO SIDE

TRAPEZIUS
P: KITE SHAPED MUSCLE, UPPER BACK
A: ROTATES INFERIOR ANGLE OF SCAPULA LATERALLY, RAISES SHOULDER, DRAWS SCAPULA BACKWARDS

SPLENIUS CAPITIS
P: MUSCLE RUNNING ALONG NECK TO TRUNK
A: EXTENDS AND ROTATES HEAD

LEVATOR SCAPULAE
P: CERVICAL VERTEBRAE TO UPPER MEDIAL BORDER OF SCAPULA
A: ROTATES AND ELEVATES SCAPULA; HELPS TO BEND NECK LATERALLY

MUSCLES OF THE TRUNK – NECK, CHEST AND ABDOMEN – ANTERIOR VIEW

KEY: P: POSITION   A: ACTION

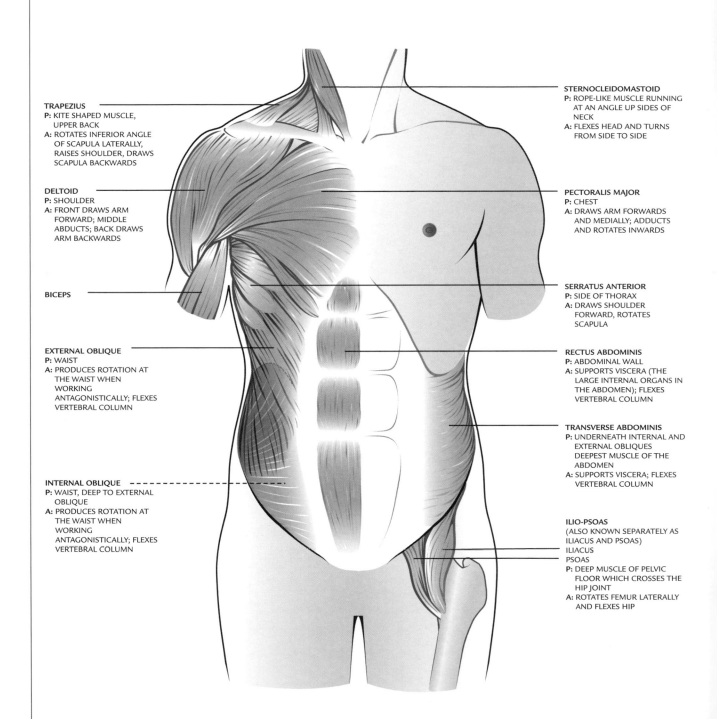

STERNOCLEIDOMASTOID
P: ROPE-LIKE MUSCLE RUNNING AT AN ANGLE UP SIDES OF NECK
A: FLEXES HEAD AND TURNS FROM SIDE TO SIDE

TRAPEZIUS
P: KITE SHAPED MUSCLE, UPPER BACK
A: ROTATES INFERIOR ANGLE OF SCAPULA LATERALLY, RAISES SHOULDER, DRAWS SCAPULA BACKWARDS

DELTOID
P: SHOULDER
A: FRONT DRAWS ARM FORWARD; MIDDLE ABDUCTS; BACK DRAWS ARM BACKWARDS

BICEPS

EXTERNAL OBLIQUE
P: WAIST
A: PRODUCES ROTATION AT THE WAIST WHEN WORKING ANTAGONISTICALLY; FLEXES VERTEBRAL COLUMN

INTERNAL OBLIQUE
P: WAIST, DEEP TO EXTERNAL OBLIQUE
A: PRODUCES ROTATION AT THE WAIST WHEN WORKING ANTAGONISTICALLY; FLEXES VERTEBRAL COLUMN

PECTORALIS MAJOR
P: CHEST
A: DRAWS ARM FORWARDS AND MEDIALLY; ADDUCTS AND ROTATES INWARDS

SERRATUS ANTERIOR
P: SIDE OF THORAX
A: DRAWS SHOULDER FORWARD, ROTATES SCAPULA

RECTUS ABDOMINIS
P: ABDOMINAL WALL
A: SUPPORTS VISCERA (THE LARGE INTERNAL ORGANS IN THE ABDOMEN); FLEXES VERTEBRAL COLUMN

TRANSVERSE ABDOMINIS
P: UNDERNEATH INTERNAL AND EXTERNAL OBLIQUES DEEPEST MUSCLE OF THE ABDOMEN
A: SUPPORTS VISCERA; FLEXES VERTEBRAL COLUMN

ILIO-PSOAS
(ALSO KNOWN SEPARATELY AS ILIACUS AND PSOAS)
ILIACUS
PSOAS
P: DEEP MUSCLE OF PELVIC FLOOR WHICH CROSSES THE HIP JOINT
A: ROTATES FEMUR LATERALLY AND FLEXES HIP

MUSCLES OF THE TRUNK – NECK, CHEST AND ABDOMEN – POSTERIOR VIEW

KEY: P: POSITION   A: ACTION

SUPERFICIAL MUSCLES

DEEP MUSCLES

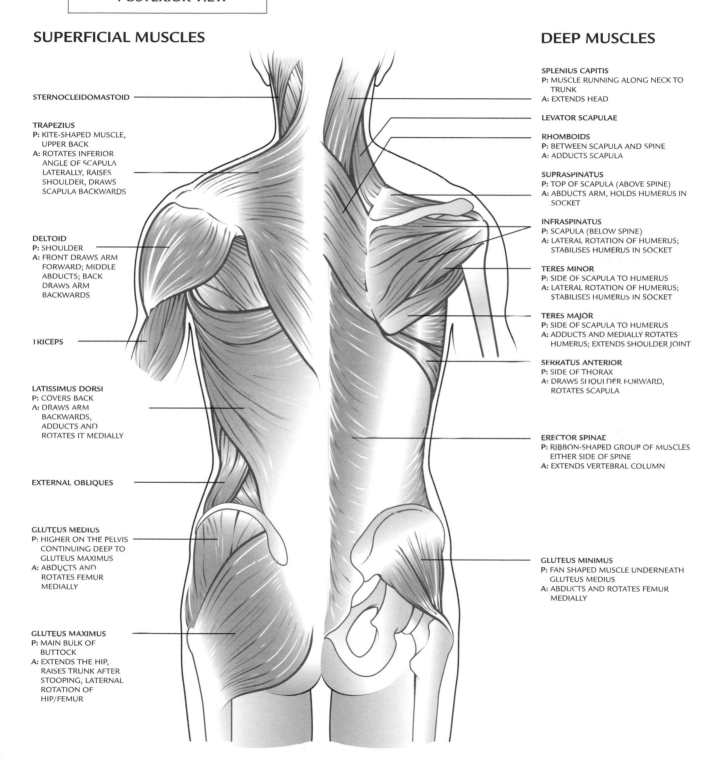

STERNOCLEIDOMASTOID

TRAPEZIUS
P: KITE-SHAPED MUSCLE, UPPER BACK
A: ROTATES INFERIOR ANGLE OF SCAPULA LATERALLY, RAISES SHOULDER, DRAWS SCAPULA BACKWARDS

DELTOID
P: SHOULDER
A: FRONT DRAWS ARM FORWARD; MIDDLE ABDUCTS; BACK DRAWS ARM BACKWARDS

TRICEPS

LATISSIMUS DORSI
P: COVERS BACK
A: DRAWS ARM BACKWARDS, ADDUCTS AND ROTATES IT MEDIALLY

EXTERNAL OBLIQUES

GLUTEUS MEDIUS
P: HIGHER ON THE PELVIS CONTINUING DEEP TO GLUTEUS MAXIMUS
A: ABDUCTS AND ROTATES FEMUR MEDIALLY

GLUTEUS MAXIMUS
P: MAIN BULK OF BUTTOCK
A: EXTENDS THE HIP, RAISES TRUNK AFTER STOOPING, LATERNAL ROTATION OF HIP/FEMUR

SPLENIUS CAPITIS
P: MUSCLE RUNNING ALONG NECK TO TRUNK
A: EXTENDS HEAD

LEVATOR SCAPULAE

RHOMBOIDS
P: BETWEEN SCAPULA AND SPINE
A: ADDUCTS SCAPULA

SUPRASPINATUS
P: TOP OF SCAPULA (ABOVE SPINE)
A: ABDUCTS ARM, HOLDS HUMERUS IN SOCKET

INFRASPINATUS
P: SCAPULA (BELOW SPINE)
A: LATERAL ROTATION OF HUMERUS; STABILISES HUMERUS IN SOCKET

TERES MINOR
P: SIDE OF SCAPULA TO HUMERUS
A: LATERAL ROTATION OF HUMERUS; STABILISES HUMERUS IN SOCKET

TERES MAJOR
P: SIDE OF SCAPULA TO HUMERUS
A: ADDUCTS AND MEDIALLY ROTATES HUMERUS; EXTENDS SHOULDER JOINT

SERRATUS ANTERIOR
P: SIDE OF THORAX
A: DRAWS SHOULDER FORWARD, ROTATES SCAPULA

ERECTOR SPINAE
P: RIBBON-SHAPED GROUP OF MUSCLES EITHER SIDE OF SPINE
A: EXTENDS VERTEBRAL COLUMN

GLUTEUS MINIMUS
P: FAN SHAPED MUSCLE UNDERNEATH GLUTEUS MEDIUS
A: ABDUCTS AND ROTATES FEMUR MEDIALLY

MUSCLES OF THE SHOULDER AND ARM – ANTERIOR VIEW

KEY: P: POSITION   A: ACTION

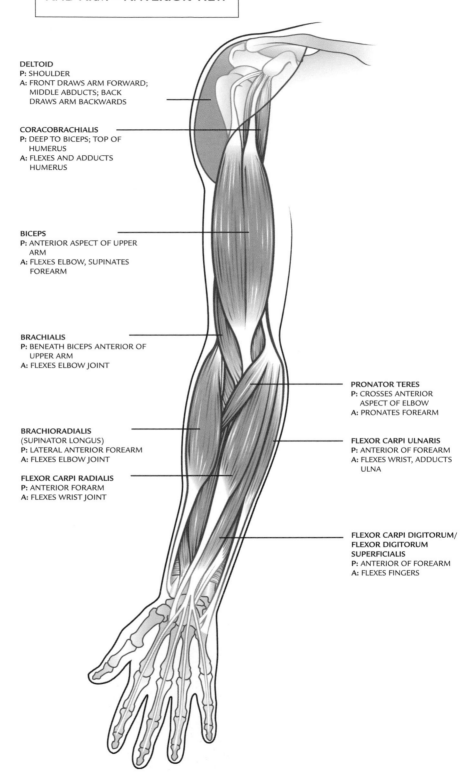

DELTOID
P: SHOULDER
A: FRONT DRAWS ARM FORWARD;
MIDDLE ABDUCTS; BACK
DRAWS ARM BACKWARDS

CORACOBRACHIALIS
P: DEEP TO BICEPS; TOP OF
HUMERUS
A: FLEXES AND ADDUCTS
HUMERUS

BICEPS
P: ANTERIOR ASPECT OF UPPER
ARM
A: FLEXES ELBOW, SUPINATES
FOREARM

BRACHIALIS
P: BENEATH BICEPS ANTERIOR OF
UPPER ARM
A: FLEXES ELBOW JOINT

BRACHIORADIALIS
(SUPINATOR LONGUS)
P: LATERAL ANTERIOR FOREARM
A: FLEXES ELBOW JOINT

FLEXOR CARPI RADIALIS
P: ANTERIOR FORARM
A: FLEXES WRIST JOINT

PRONATOR TERES
P: CROSSES ANTERIOR
ASPECT OF ELBOW
A: PRONATES FOREARM

FLEXOR CARPI ULNARIS
P: ANTERIOR OF FOREARM
A: FLEXES WRIST, ADDUCTS
ULNA

**FLEXOR CARPI DIGITORUM/
FLEXOR DIGITORUM
SUPERFICIALIS**
P: ANTERIOR OF FOREARM
A: FLEXES FINGERS

MUSCLES OF THE SHOULDER AND ARM – POSTERIOR VIEW

KEY: P: POSITION   A: ACTION

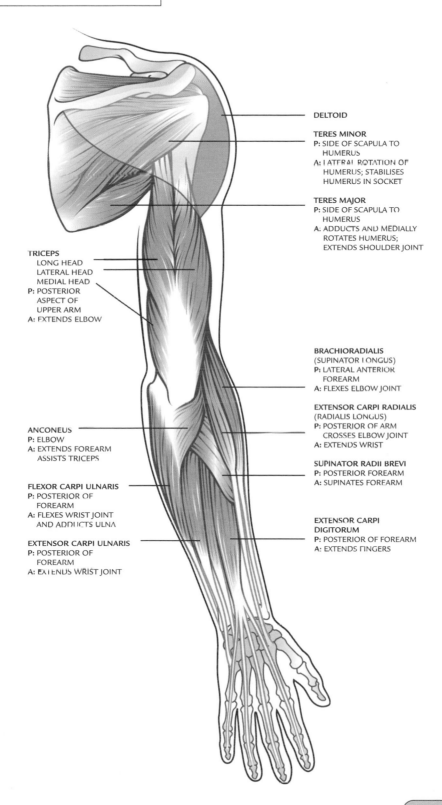

DELTOID

TERES MINOR
P: SIDE OF SCAPULA TO HUMERUS
A: LATERAL ROTATION OF HUMERUS; STABILISES HUMERUS IN SOCKET

TERES MAJOR
P: SIDE OF SCAPULA TO HUMERUS
A: ADDUCTS AND MEDIALLY ROTATES HUMERUS; EXTENDS SHOULDER JOINT

TRICEPS
LONG HEAD
LATERAL HEAD
MEDIAL HEAD
P: POSTERIOR ASPECT OF UPPER ARM
A: EXTENDS ELBOW

BRACHIORADIALIS
(SUPINATOR LONGUS)
P: LATERAL ANTERIOR FOREARM
A: FLEXES ELBOW JOINT

EXTENSOR CARPI RADIALIS
(RADIALIS LONGUS)
P: POSTERIOR OF ARM CROSSES ELBOW JOINT
A: EXTENDS WRIST

SUPINATOR RADII BREVI
P: POSTERIOR FOREARM
A: SUPINATES FOREARM

ANCONEUS
P: ELBOW
A: EXTENDS FOREARM ASSISTS TRICEPS

FLEXOR CARPI ULNARIS
P: POSTERIOR OF FOREARM
A: FLEXES WRIST JOINT AND ADDUCTS ULNA

EXTENSOR CARPI DIGITORUM
P: POSTERIOR OF FOREARM
A: EXTENDS FINGERS

EXTENSOR CARPI ULNARIS
P: POSTERIOR OF FOREARM
A: EXTENDS WRIST JOINT

THE MUSCULAR SYSTEM

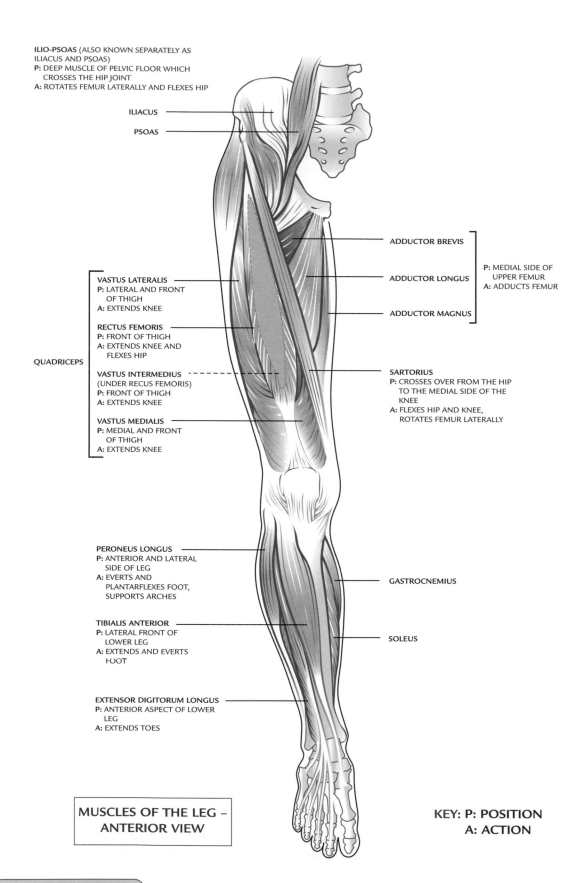

ILIO-PSOAS (ALSO KNOWN SEPARATELY AS ILIACUS AND PSOAS)
P: DEEP MUSCLE OF PELVIC FLOOR WHICH CROSSES THE HIP JOINT
A: ROTATES FEMUR LATERALLY AND FLEXES HIP

ILIACUS

PSOAS

ADDUCTOR BREVIS

ADDUCTOR LONGUS

ADDUCTOR MAGNUS

P: MEDIAL SIDE OF UPPER FEMUR
A: ADDUCTS FEMUR

VASTUS LATERALIS
P: LATERAL AND FRONT OF THIGH
A: EXTENDS KNEE

RECTUS FEMORIS
P: FRONT OF THIGH
A: EXTENDS KNEE AND FLEXES HIP

QUADRICEPS

VASTUS INTERMEDIUS
(UNDER RECUS FEMORIS)
P: FRONT OF THIGH
A: EXTENDS KNEE

VASTUS MEDIALIS
P: MEDIAL AND FRONT OF THIGH
A: EXTENDS KNEE

SARTORIUS
P: CROSSES OVER FROM THE HIP TO THE MEDIAL SIDE OF THE KNEE
A: FLEXES HIP AND KNEE, ROTATES FEMUR LATERALLY

PERONEUS LONGUS
P: ANTERIOR AND LATERAL SIDE OF LEG
A: EVERTS AND PLANTARFLEXES FOOT, SUPPORTS ARCHES

GASTROCNEMIUS

TIBIALIS ANTERIOR
P: LATERAL FRONT OF LOWER LEG
A: EXTENDS AND EVERTS FOOT

SOLEUS

EXTENSOR DIGITORUM LONGUS
P: ANTERIOR ASPECT OF LOWER LEG
A: EXTENDS TOES

MUSCLES OF THE LEG – ANTERIOR VIEW

KEY: P: POSITION
A: ACTION

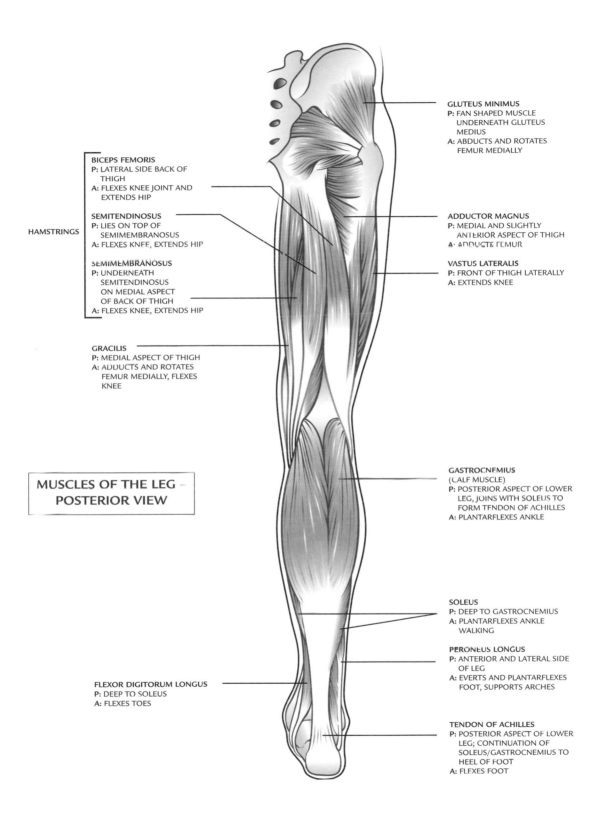

GLUTEUS MINIMUS
P: FAN SHAPED MUSCLE
UNDERNEATH GLUTEUS
MEDIUS
A: ABDUCTS AND ROTATES
FEMUR MEDIALLY

HAMSTRINGS

BICEPS FEMORIS
P: LATERAL SIDE BACK OF
THIGH
A: FLEXES KNEE JOINT AND
EXTENDS HIP

SEMITENDINOSUS
P: LIES ON TOP OF
SEMIMEMBRANOSUS
A: FLEXES KNEE, EXTENDS HIP

SEMIMEMBRANOSUS
P: UNDERNEATH
SEMITENDINOSUS
ON MEDIAL ASPECT
OF BACK OF THIGH
A: FLEXES KNEE, EXTENDS HIP

GRACILIS
P: MEDIAL ASPECT OF THIGH
A: ADDUCTS AND ROTATES
FEMUR MEDIALLY, FLEXES
KNEE

ADDUCTOR MAGNUS
P: MEDIAL AND SLIGHTLY
ANTERIOR ASPECT OF THIGH
A: ADDUCTS FEMUR

VASTUS LATERALIS
P: FRONT OF THIGH LATERALLY
A: EXTENDS KNEE

GASTROCNEMIUS
(CALF MUSCLE)
P: POSTERIOR ASPECT OF LOWER
LEG, JOINS WITH SOLEUS TO
FORM TENDON OF ACHILLES
A: PLANTARFLEXES ANKLE

**MUSCLES OF THE LEG –
POSTERIOR VIEW**

SOLEUS
P: DEEP TO GASTROCNEMIUS
A: PLANTARFLEXES ANKLE
WALKING

PERONEUS LONGUS
P: ANTERIOR AND LATERAL SIDE
OF LEG
A: EVERTS AND PLANTARFLEXES
FOOT, SUPPORTS ARCHES

FLEXOR DIGITORUM LONGUS
P: DEEP TO SOLEUS
A: FLEXES TOES

TENDON OF ACHILLES
P: POSTERIOR ASPECT OF LOWER
LEG; CONTINUATION OF
SOLEUS/GASTROCNEMIUS TO
HEEL OF FOOT
A: FLEXES FOOT

*You now know all the characteristics, functions, positions and actions of healthy skeletal
muscles. The next section summarises common problems that occur in the muscular system.*

DISEASES AND DISORDERS

Fibrositis
Cause: build-up of lactic acid inside muscles.
Effect: inflammation of soft tissues and stiffness and pain. Lumbago – fibrositis of muscles in lumbar region of back; torticollis, known as 'wry neck' – fibrositis of the sterno-cleido mastoid muscle causes head to sit to one side.

Cramp
Cause: vigorous exercise and over-exertion; also extreme heat; sodium and/or water depletion.
Effect: painful localised and involuntary contraction of one or more muscles.

Atony
Lack of normal tone or tension in a muscle.

Atrophy
Cause: undernourishment; lack of use.
Effect: wasting away, or failure to reach normal size, of bulk of muscle.

Myositis
Inflammation of a muscle.

Rupture
Burst or tear in the fascia or sheath surrounding muscles.

Spasm
A more than usual number of muscle fibres in sustained contraction, usually in response to pain. Fibres contract for much longer than is usually necessary.

Spasticity
Cause: inhibitory nerves have been cut.
Effect: spinal reflexes cause sustained contraction.

Sprain
Cause: sudden twist or wrench of the joint's ligaments
Effect: an injury or damage to a joint; painful swelling of the joint; the most commonly sprained joint is the ankle (often called a 'twisted ankle'). A sprained ankle is usually caused by the joint 'going over', thus putting all the body weight on the ankle.

Strain
Cause: overexertion, over-stretching, over-use; failure to warm up before strenuous activity, especially sport.
Effect: an injury to a muscle or its tendon; may occasionally involve rupture (tearing) of muscle fibres, muscle sheath or tendon.

Stress
Cause: stress is any factor which affects physical or mental well-being.
Effect: excessive muscle tension and subsequent muscle pain, especially in the back and neck.

Interrelationships
Muscular system links to:
Nervous: relies upon nerve impulses to produce a contraction in the muscle. Without nerve stimulus movement would not be possible.
Skeletal: muscles always cross a joint and thus rely on the skeletal system for leverage and movement.
Digestive: nutrition/energy in the form of glucose is received from the digestive system. If it is not immediately used it is converted to glycogen and stored in the muscle fibres for energy production later.
Circulatory and respiratory: muscles receive oxygen from the vascular and respiratory system.

SUMMARY

- *There are three types of muscle: voluntary, involuntary and cardiac.*
- *There are two types of muscle attachment: tendon and fascia.*
- *Voluntary muscles have a variety of actions.*
- *Muscles work by contraction.*
- *Over-contraction without enough oxygen can cause lactic acid to form, which prevents muscles from functioning correctly.*

The Circulatory (Vascular) System

The circulatory or vascular system is composed of the blood, the heart, arteries and veins of the coronary, pulmonary, portal and systemic systems.

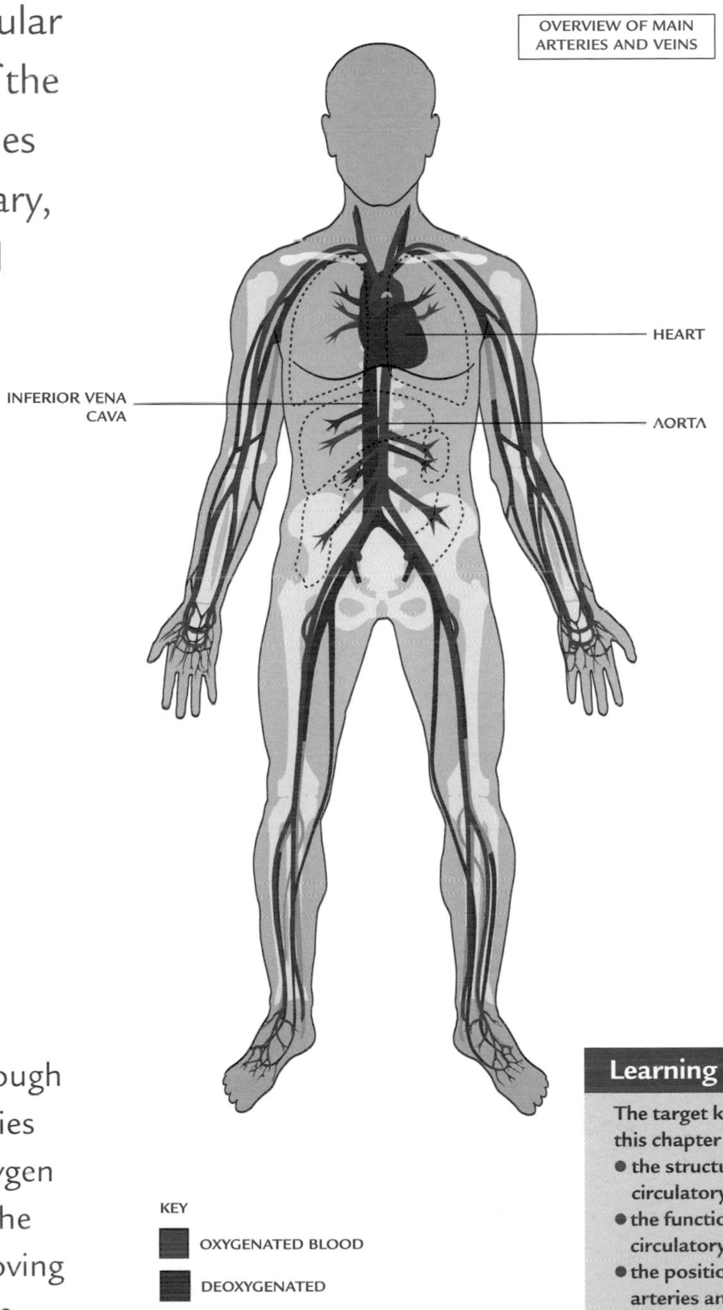

OVERVIEW OF MAIN ARTERIES AND VEINS

HEART

INFERIOR VENA CAVA

AORTA

In Brief

Blood is pumped from the heart around the body through a transport system of arteries and veins. It distributes oxygen and essential nutrients to the whole body as well as removing potentially damaging waste products and carbon dioxide.

KEY

OXYGENATED BLOOD

DEOXYGENATED

Learning objectives

The target knowledge of this chapter is:
- the structure of the circulatory system
- the function of the circulatory system
- the position of the main arteries and veins in the body
- diseases and disorders.

WHAT IS BLOOD?

A fluid connective tissue made up of plasma and cells. Adult bodies contain approximately 4-5 litres whereas a new-born baby has only 300ml. It is alkaline (pH7.4).

What does it do?
- transports oxygen, nutrients, hormones and enzymes around the body.
- transports waste materials from the body to the organs of excretion.
- helps fight infection (with leucocytes and antibodies – see opposite for more detail).
- prevents the loss of body fluids after accidents by clotting.
- regulates body temperature.

What is it made of?
A: Plasma
Plasma makes up 55% of blood volume. It is a slightly thick, straw-coloured fluid. It is mostly water (90-92%) and the rest is plasma proteins (albumin, globulin, fibrinogen and prothrombin).

Plasma helps to transport the following essential substances around the body:
- **mineral salts** – sodium chloride, commonly known as table salt, sodium carbonate and the salts of potassium, magnesium, phosphorus, calcium, iron, copper, iodine – which help nerve conduction and ensure that tissue cells keep the right acid balance.
- **nutrients** – amino acids, fatty acids, glucose, glycerol, vitamins. Most of these come from digested food and are absorbed (by the plasma proteins in blood) from the intestines to be used by cell tissues for energy, repair and cell reproduction.
- **waste** – waste products (like urea) are transported to the liver for breakdown, and then to the kidneys for excretion (eventually from the bladder as urine)
- **hormones** – chemical messengers produced by the endocrine glands. Plasma transports them to various organs and their job is then to change or influence that organ's activity or behaviour.
- **enzymes** – the chemical catalysts in the body. They produce or speed up chemical changes in other substances but remain unchanged themselves.
- **gases** – oxygen and CO_2 are dissolved in plasma.
- **antibodies and antitoxins** – the body's protectors. These complex proteins are produced in the lymph glands in response to the presence of toxins released by viruses and bacteria. Each antibody/antitoxin attacks a specific toxin (also known as antigen).

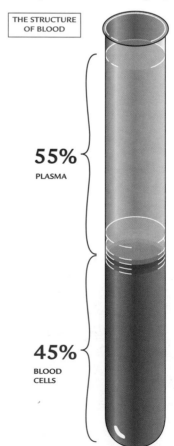

THE STRUCTURE OF BLOOD

55%
PLASMA

45%
BLOOD CELLS

B: Cells

There are three types of blood cells:

Erythrocytes

(also known as red corpuscles/blood cells)

Structure: biconcave, nucleus-free discs

Function: transport oxygen as oxyhaemoglobin (for which iron and vitamin B12 are required).

General characteristics:

- produced in red bone marrow
- give blood its characteristic red colour, thanks to a protein called haemoglobin which absorbs oxygen
- life span of about 120 days
- broken down in the spleen and then the liver (where any spare iron is retrieved and recycled).

Leucocytes

(also known as white corpuscles/blood cells)

There are two main types – granulocytes and non-granular leucocytes.

Structure: larger than erythrocytes, with an irregular shape and a nucleus

Function: to protect the body from infection.

General characteristics:

- approximately 8000 per mm³ in a healthy body
- increase rapidly by mitosis in cases of serious infection.

Specific characteristics of granulocytes:

- defend system against micro-organisms (e.g. viruses and bacteria)
- form 75% of white blood cells
- attracted by toxins into the tissues and can pass through capillary walls.

Specific characteristics of non-granular leucocytes:

- **lymphocytes** – some produce antibodies; formed in lymphatic tissue and found in all tissue except brain and spinal cord
- **monocytes** – eat bacteria and other micro-organisms (a process known as phagocytosis).

Thrombocytes

(also known as platelets)

Structure: small, fragile cells with no nucleus

Function: responsible for blood clotting.

General characteristics:

- formed in red bone marrow
- 250 000 per mm³ of blood.

You now know what blood is made of and what it does. The next section explains how it moves around the human body, starting with the heart.

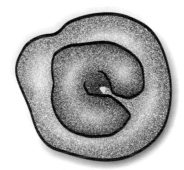

**LYMPHOCYTE
(WHITE BLOOD CELL)**

**ERYTHROCYTES
(RED BLOOD CELLS)**

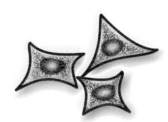

**THROMBOCYTES
(PLATELETS)**

THE CIRCULATORY (VASCULAR) SYSTEM

THE HEART & SYSTEMS OF CIRCULATION

Section A: the structure and function of the heart

How does blood circulate?

Blood is pumped from the heart (a muscular organ) around the body through a transport system of arteries, veins and capillaries. Pulmonary circulation is the transport of blood from the heart to the lungs and back again; systemic circulation is the transport of blood from the heart to the rest of the body and back. The blood circulation is two closed systems.

What is the heart?

The heart is the centre of the circulatory system (hence the use of the word heart to mean centre in English). If blood is the body's fuel, the heart is its engine.

What does the heart look like?

It is a hollow red organ, approximately the size of its owner's fist, positioned in the centre of the thorax and divided into four chambers. These are the right and left atria (or auricles) in the upper part, and the right and left ventricles in the lower part. Atria and ventricles are connected by the atrioventricular opening. The septum, a muscular wall, separates the right and left sides of the heart. This prevents blood from the veins (known as venous blood) on the right coming into contact with blood going to the arteries (known as arterial blood) on the left.

● Useful Tip

In order to remember which chambers are atria and which are ventricles, and how blood moves between them, think of their position in the alphabet: *a* comes before *v* just as blood enters the atrium before the ventricle.

KEY
1. SUPERIOR VENA CAVA
2. AORTIC ARCH
3. DESCENDING AORTA
4. INFERIOR VENA CAVA
5. AORTA
6. RIGHT ATRIUM
7. RIGHT VENTRICLE
8. LEFT ATRIUM
9. LEFT VENTRICLE
10. SEPTUM
11. PULMONARY VALVE
12. PULMONARY ARTERIES
13. PULMONARY VEINS
14. MITRAL (BICUSPID) VALVE
15. TRICUSPID VALVE

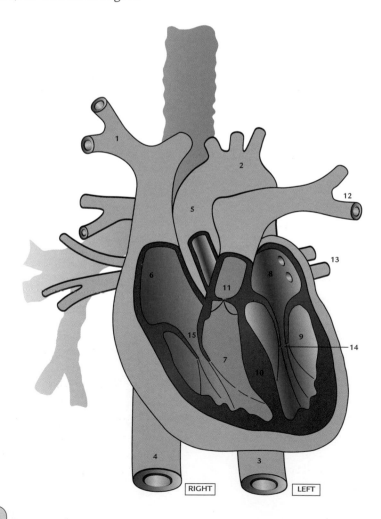

RIGHT   LEFT

The heart has a muscular wall with membranes covering and lining it. The wall is divided into three layers:

- **endocardium**: the inner layer, made of epithelial tissue which provides a friction-free surface for the chambers of the heart

- **myocardium**: the middle layer. This is the thickest layer and it is made of cardiac muscle

- **pericardium**: the outer layer. This consists of two layers which cover the outside of the heart. The inner layer is serous membrane, made of epithelial tissue which provides a friction-free surface for the chambers of the heart, while the outer layer is a fibrous structure which helps to keep the heart in the right position in the chest.

What does the heart do?

The heart is the pump that drives the whole circulatory system. It receives and propels blood, rhythmically contracting, forcing the blood through a system of vessels. The heart's action is controlled by the autonomic nervous system.

What is a heartbeat?

The heartbeat, or cardiac cycle, is the pattern of muscular contraction of the heart wall:

- both the atria contract, forcing their contents into the ventricles
- the atria relax but the ventricles contract, emptying their contents into the arteries
- the ventricles relax and the heart is at rest.

While resting the heart dilates and fills with blood. The period of rest (diastole) equals the period of contraction (systole). The heartbeat (or cycle) starts at a point in the right atrium called the pacemaker (sino-atrial node). This consists of

specialised neuromuscular tissue which is supplied by the autonomic nervous system. From here, the contraction of the heart muscle spreads through the atria and then down the septum to the walls of the ventricles.

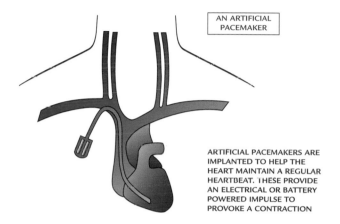

AN ARTIFICIAL PACEMAKER

ARTIFICIAL PACEMAKERS ARE IMPLANTED TO HELP THE HEART MAINTAIN A REGULAR HEARTBEAT. THESE PROVIDE AN ELECTRICAL OR BATTERY POWERED IMPULSE TO PROVOKE A CONTRACTION

What is a pulse?

When you feel your pulse, you are feeling the rate at which your heart pumps blood through your circulatory system. Technically, it is a wave of artery wall distension. When blood is pumped from the left ventricle into the aorta, the aorta distends, i.e. swells. The elastic wall of the aorta then recoils thus forcing the blood to move on. This sets up a wave of swelling and contracting which continues along all the elastic arteries. What we think of as a pulse is in fact this wave, which can be felt wherever an artery passes close to the surface of the skin and over a bone. Since the pulse varies with the heartbeat, the pulse is taken to check if a heart is beating normally.

Is the heartbeat always the same?

The heartbeat changes in both healthy and unhealthy bodies, for a variety of reasons. The following all affect it:

- **exercise**: increases the rate of the heartbeat (and rest slows it down again)

Did you know?

Most adults heartbeat is 72-80 beats per minute whereas most babies have a beat of 130 times a minute.

Did you know?

In one lifetime, a heart will beat approximately 2,700,000,000 times.

THE CIRCULATORY (VASCULAR) SYSTEM

- **age**: heartbeat is faster in infants and slows gradually as age increases
- **size of the heart**: a smaller heart may have a faster heartbeat and a larger heart a slower heartbeat
- **emotions and excitement**: increase the heartbeat, first through nervous stimuli and then through an increase in the level of adrenaline

- **temperament**: a placid, slow heartbeat is not easily varied whereas an excitable person will have a quicker heartbeat which changes easily
- **disease**: the heartbeat is quickened by fever, haemorrhage, hyper-thyroidism and slowed by jaundice, heart block and pressure on the brain.

Section B: the circulation in the heart – pulmonary and coronary

What is pulmonary circulation?

The circulation of blood from the heart to the lungs and back. Deoxygenated blood travels from the heart to the lungs in the pulmonary artery. The blood gets rid of its carbon dioxide (CO_2) and replaces it with oxygen. It then returns to the heart via the pulmonary veins (from lungs to heart) ready to be pumped around the body.

How does this happen?

The right atrium receives deoxygenated blood from the superior vena cava (the vein from the upper body) and the inferior vena cava (the vein from the lower body). The blood then flows into the right ventricle from where it is pumped into the pulmonary artery which divides into the right and left pulmonary arteries (which go to the right and left lungs). Blood reaches the lungs via tiny vessels called capillaries which are porous to gases (*see The Respiratory System p. 116*). The lungs remove the CO_2 from the blood in the capillaries, replace it with oxygen and return the oxygenated blood to the left atrium of the heart through the four pulmonary veins. The blood is pushed by the contraction of the left atrium through the bicuspid valve into the left ventricle. The left ventricle then contracts and pumps the blood through the aorta, which branches to form the ascending and descending aorta, for distribution around the body.

How is the direction of the blood correctly maintained?

The direction of blood is maintained by valves. The atrioventricular openings each have a valve: the tricuspid valve on the right and the bicuspid valve on the left. Both these valves allow blood to flow from the atria into the ventricles, but block the atria when the ventricles contract, ensuring that blood continues to circulate in the correct direction. The semi-lunar valves (three pocket-shaped flaps at the vessel's entrance) in the aorta and the pulmonary artery, ensure that there is no back flow from the aorta to the left ventricle or from the pulmonary artery into the right ventricle.

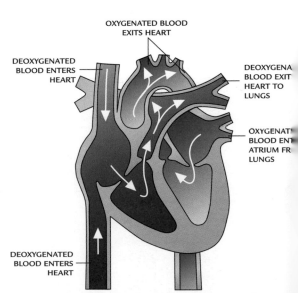

OXYGENATED BLOOD EXITS HEART

DEOXYGENATED BLOOD ENTERS HEART

DEOXYGENA[TED] BLOOD EXIT[S] HEART TO LUNGS

OXYGENAT[ED] BLOOD ENT[ERS] ATRIUM FR[OM] LUNGS

DEOXYGENATED BLOOD ENTERS HEART

DIAGRAM SHOWING FLOW OF BLOOD THROUGH THE HEART

What is coronary circulation?

The heart is, of course, a muscle which needs the benefits of circulation like every other muscle and organ in the body. It has its own circulatory system called coronary circulation. Right and left coronary arteries leave the beginning of the aorta and branch within the heart wall to form a network of capillaries to feed the tissue cells. The blood is then collected back into the coronary veins which empty into the right atrium of the heart.

You now know how blood is pumped into and out of the heart. The following section explains how it travels from the heart around the body.

Section C: circulation in the body – systemic and portal

What is systemic circulation?

Systemic circulation is the circulation of blood from the heart to the body. Blood leaves the heart by the aorta, the largest artery in the body, travels throughout the body and returns to the heart through the inferior and superior venae cavae (two of the largest veins). An extensive network of arteries, veins and capillaries transports blood to every cell in the body.

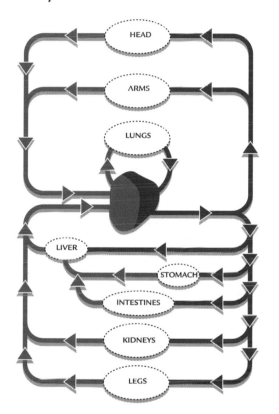

DEOXYGENATED BLOOD

OXYGENATED BLOOD

WHAT IS PORTAL CIRCULATION?

The veins from the stomach, spleen, pancreas and intestines join to form the hepatic-portal vein which carries blood into the liver.

LIVER

STOMACH

INTESTINES

What do arteries and veins do?

Arteries carry oxygenated blood from the heart and veins carry deoxygenated blood to the heart, except in the pulmonary system.

Arteries

Structure: arteries are thick-walled, hollow tubes. They all have the same basic construction:

● a fibrous outer covering
● a middle layer of muscle and elastic tissue
● an endothelial layer made of squamous epithelial tissue.

The quantity of muscle and elastic tissue in the middle layer depends on the size of the artery and its distance from the heart because arteries need to expand in order to propel blood along. Small arteries further from the heart have more muscle and less elastic tissue (because there is less blood to transport). The muscle tissue helps to maintain blood pressure and keeps blood moving around the body. The movement of the blood maintains potency (the openness of the vessel). Large arteries branch into small arteries which branch into arterioles which branch into capillaries.

Function: arteries (apart from the pulmonary artery) carry oxygenated blood from the heart to the body. The pulmonary artery carries deoxygenated blood to the lungs.

Arterioles

Structure: arterioles are a smaller version of arteries. They have a similar structure, though the middle layer of the walls is mainly involuntary muscle tissue (i.e. it has no control). This muscle is supplied with vasomotor nerves through which the vessel is contracted or relaxed. Under normal conditions all the arterioles are slightly contracted which helps to maintain blood pressure.

Functions: when a large blood supply is required by an active organ the arterioles relax and dilate to provide it (e.g. muscles during exercise, the stomach and intestines after eating and the skin when the body temperature rises). They contract when an organ is at rest.

General characteristics:

● the hormones adrenaline, noradrenaline and vasopressin (antidiuretic hormone) may cause the arterioles to contract
● in cases of shock, all the arterioles relax and blood pressure is very low. This is a dangerous condition.

Capillaries

Structure: capillaries are the smallest blood vessels. Their walls are one cell thick (i.e. microscopic) and porous, thus allowing the passage of gases (like oxygen and carbon dioxide) and nutrients. A large amount of water, plus the solutions dissolved in it, filters out through the capillary walls and bathes the body tissues. This liquid is called interstitial fluid. It carries food, vitamins, mineral salts and hormones out to the tissues and collects waste products, especially carbon dioxide and urea, from them. Most of the fluid then returns to the capillaries before they join up to become venules.

Function: to distribute essential oxygen and nutrients to most parts of the body. Capillaries supply every part of the body except the deep brain, the hyaline cartilage and the epidermis.

Venules

Structure: venules are small veins. These have a thin wall with a large passage (lumen) to carry the blood so they are easily collapsed under pressure.
Function: they carry deoxygenated blood from the capillaries to the larger veins.

Veins

Structure: veins have three-layered walls and though the basic structure is similar to that of arteries, their walls are much thinner and the lumen (the passage in the centre which carries the blood) is much larger. They vary in size, the largest being the venae cavae (from the body into the heart) and the pulmonary vein (from the lungs to the heart). The action of skeletal muscles pushes blood through the vessels. Valves in the endothelial layer of the veins prevent a back flow of blood. Blood pressure in veins is very low so these valves are essential.

Function: veins carry deoxygenated blood back to the heart (apart from the pulmonary vein).

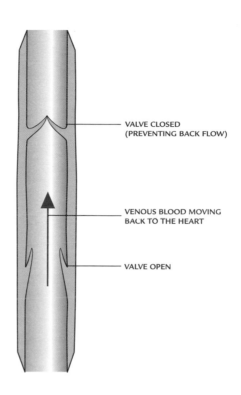

VALVE CLOSED
(PREVENTING BACK FLOW)

VENOUS BLOOD MOVING
BACK TO THE HEART

VALVE OPEN

The table shows the different characteristics of arteries and veins

Characteristics of arteries	Characteristics of veins
Transport blood from heart	Transport blood to the heart
Oxygenated blood (not pulmonary)	Deoxygenated blood (not pulmonary)
Lumen (passage) is small	Lumen (passage) is large
Pumped by heart and muscle tissue in artery wall	Pumped by skeletal muscle pump and the presence of valves
Thick, muscular and elastic walls	Thin walls, not muscular or elastic
Arterial blood contains a high concentration of nutrients	Venous blood contains a high concentration of waste products

Main veins and arteries

The circulations begin at the heart. The inferior and superior venae cavae bring venous blood into the right atrium, the pulmonary veins bring arterial blood into the left atrium. The pulmonary arteries take blood to the lungs. The aorta, the main artery in the body, carries arterial blood to the body. It branches upwards to form the ascending aorta, which takes blood to the upper body (arms and head) and downwards, to form the descending aorta, taking blood to the rest of the body. Usually the names of veins correspond to the names of the arteries and they generally follow the same course, albeit in a different direction. When the blood reaches the various branches it is distributed through a network of arteries, arterioles and capillaries. The capillaries, the last vessels to distribute oxygenated blood, join the first vessels to collect deoxygenated blood, also called capillaries, which link up to form venules which feed into a network of veins taking the blood back to the heart for reoxygenation.

You now know what blood is, how it moves and where it goes. The following section shows the different parts of the body and the names of the main veins and arteries which feed each one.

THE CIRCULATORY (VASCULAR) SYSTEM

MAIN ARTERIES AND VEINS OF THE BODY

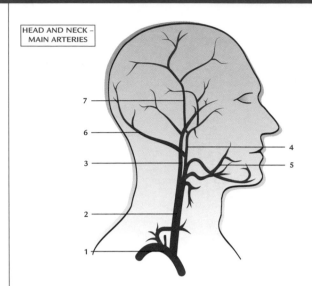

HEAD AND NECK – MAIN ARTERIES

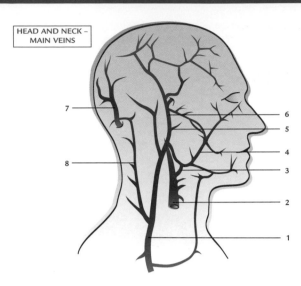

HEAD AND NECK – MAIN VEINS

1. INNOMINATE ARTERY
2. COMMON CAROTID ARTERY
3. INTERNAL CAROTID
4. EXTERNAL CAROTID
5. FACIAL
6. OCCIPITAL
7. SUPERFICIAL TEMPORAL

1. EXTERNAL JUGULAR
2. INTERNAL JUGULAR
3. COMMON FACIAL
4. ANTERIOR FACIAL
5. MAXILLARY
6. SUPERFICIAL TEMPORAL
7. OCCIPITAL
8. POSTERIOR EXTERNAL JUGULAR

TRUNK – MAIN ARTERIES AND VEINS

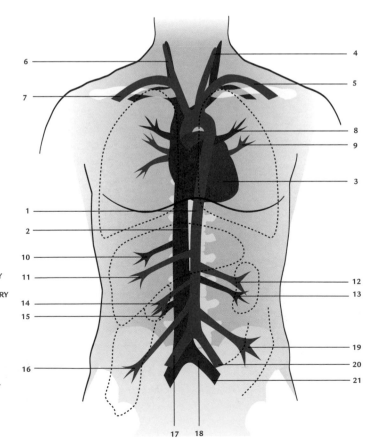

1. DESCENDING AORTA
2. INFERIOR VENA CAVA
3. HEART
4. LEFT COMMON CAROTID ARTERY
5. LEFT SUBCLAVIAN ARTERY
6. RIGHT COMMON CAROTID ARTERY
7. RIGHT SUBCLAVIAN ARTERY
8. 2 PULMONARY ARTERIES
9. 2 PULMONARY VEINS
10. RIGHT HEPATIC VEIN
11. RIGHT HEPATIC ARTERY
12. SPLENIC ARTERY
13. SPLENIC VEIN
14. RIGHT RENAL ARTERY
15. RIGHT RENAL VEIN
16. SUPERIOR MESENTERIC ARTERY
17. RIGHT ILIAC ARTERY
18. RIGHT ILIAC VEIN
19. INFERIOR MESENTERIC ARTERY
20. LEFT ILIAC ARTERY
21. LEFT ILIAC VEIN

1. RIGHT SUBCLAVIAN
2. RIGHT COMMON CAROTID
3. VERTEBRAL
4. AXILLARY
5. BRACHIAL
6. RIGHT ULNAR
7. RIGHT RADIAL
8. RIGHT DEEP PALMAR ARCH
9. RIGHT SUPERFICIAL
   PALMAR ARCH

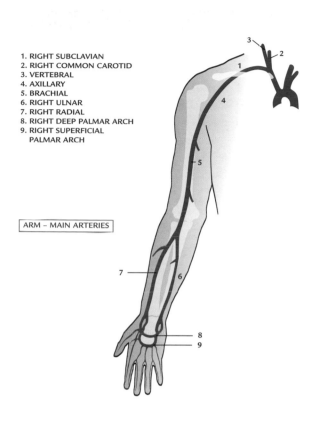

ARM – MAIN ARTERIES

1. RIGHT AXILLARY
2. RIGHT BRACHIAL
3. RIGHT BASILIC
4. RIGHT CEPHALIC
5. RIGHT SUBCLAVIAN

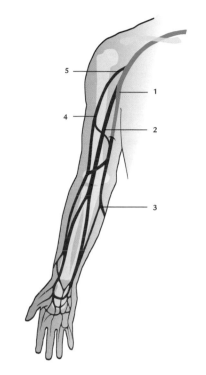

ARM – MAIN VEINS

1. EXTERNAL ILIAC
2. LEFT FEMORAL
3. LEFT POPLITEAL
4. LEFT ANTERIOR
   TIBIAL
5. LEFT POSTERIOR
   TIBIAL
6. PLANTAR ARCH

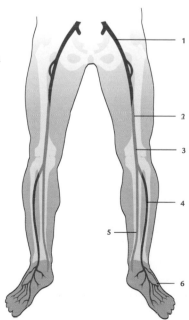

LEG – MAIN
ARTERIES

1. LONG SAPHENOUS
2. LEFT SHORT SAPHENOUS
3. DORSAL VENOUS ARCH
4. LEFT FEMORAL
5. LEFT POPLITEAL
6. RIGHT POSTERIOR TIBIAL
7. RIGHT ANTERIOR TIBIAL

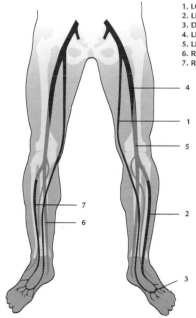

LEG – MAIN
VEINS

THE CIRCULATORY (VASCULAR) SYSTEM

BLOCK PRESSURE

If you have ever visited the doctor in the UK, you will probably have had your blood pressure checked. But what is it and how does it affect the circulation?

What is blood pressure?

The force that the blood exerts on the walls of the blood vessels as transmitted from the heart. Without pressure blood would not move at all. Blood is always under pressure but the amount of pressure varies in different types of blood vessels: high blood pressure in the arteries gradually becomes lower in the capillaries and veins. In the large veins approaching the heart there is negative pressure. The heartbeat also affects blood pressure: when the ventricle is contracting it is high, when the ventricle is dilating it is low.

What factors produce and maintain pressure?

- **cardiac output**: pumped out of the left ventricle
- **resistance offered by the arterioles**: contraction is controlled by the vasomotor nerves and by adrenaline and noradrenaline. The greater the contraction the higher the blood pressure.
- **total blood volume**: if the amount of circulating blood is reduced, blood pressure is lowered; if there is too much retention of fluid (oedema), blood pressure is raised.
- **viscosity of blood**: this depends partly on the plasma, especially the amount of plasma proteins and also on the number of erythrocytes. The lower the viscosity, the lower the blood pressure.
- **elasticity of artery walls**: if the arteries harden there is a loss of elasticity and pressure is raised. If the arteries soften, there is lower pressure.

● Useful Tip

How do you remember which is low and which is high blood pressure? Think of the 'o': l-o-w is hyp-o.

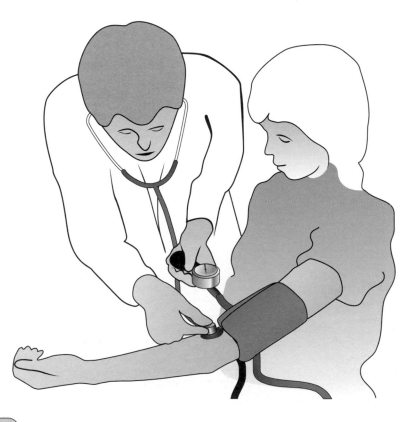

Blood pressure is given as two readings:
- **systolic**: when the heart is contracting pressure reaches its peak level
- **diastolic**: when the heart is relaxing (dilating) pressure reaches its lowest level.

A blood pressure reading of 100/70 means that systolic pressure is 100 and diastolic pressure is 70.

How are they measured?

Blood pressure is measured with a sphygmomanometer. The patient's upper arm is encircled by an inflatable rubber bag contained in a cuff connected to a pressure pump and manometer. By pumping up the bag, the pressure is raised to 20-30mm of mercury pressure (Hg) which is sufficient to constrict the brachial artery so no blood can pass through and the radial pulse disappears. The pressure is then lowered to a point where the pulse can be felt. At this point the pressure

shown on the column of mercury is considered to be the systolic pressure. The diastolic pressure reading is taken when the sound of the pulse fades.

Causes and effects of high and low blood pressure

Hypertension (high blood pressure)

Causes: stress, medication, kidney disease, narrowing or hardening of the arteries, smoking, alcohol, diet and hereditary factors.

Effects: angina, heart attack, strokes, kidney complaints.

Hypotension (low blood pressure)

Causes: underactive adrenal glands, hereditary factors; shock may cause short term hypotension.

Effects: dizziness; fainting.

BLOOD CLOTTING

HOW DOES BLOOD CLOT?

If a blood vessel (a capillary, vein or artery) is damaged (internally or externally) bleeding occurs until a clot forms. This clot stops excessive loss of blood from the system. If no blood clot forms it is called a haemorrhage. The following diagram shows the four stages of clot formation.

 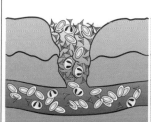 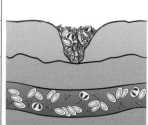 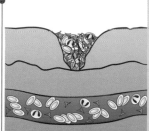

1 *Thrombocytes (platelets) are easily damaged and if a blood vessel wall is broken they disintegrate and release an enzyme called thromboplastin.*

2 *Thromboplastin then converts a plasma protein called prothrombin into an active enzyme called thrombin. Calcium is needed for this process to work. (Thus thromboplastin + calcium + prothrombin = thrombin).*

3 *Thrombin then changes another plasma protein, fibrinogen into fibrin. Fibrin is insoluble and forms a net-like covering across the damaged vessel. (Thus thrombin + fibrinogen = fibrin).*

4 *As blood tries to flow through the net, the red and white cells and platelets are trapped and form a clot. The additional fluid that remains is known as serum. (Thus fibrin + blood cells = clot).*

THE CIRCULATORY (VASCULAR) SYSTEM

The following are necessary for a clot to form:
● prothrombin
● calcium
● thromboplastin (produced by damaged platelets)
● fibrin
● vitamin K (necessary for formation of prothrombin)

Blood clotting can be affected by:
● a deficiency of platelets as in severe bone marrow diseases
● lack of one of the necessary components listed above (causing diseases such as haemophilia)
● an absence of fibrinogen
● lack of Vitamin K which is necessary for the production of prothrombin
● lack of calcium
● an excess of fibrinogen in the blood can cause thrombosis (internal and potentially dangerous blood clots).

Finally, blood types. All human blood is the same in terms of composition and function. But four different types exist, the discovery of which made blood transfusions much more successful.

What are blood types?

In 1902 an Austrian physician named Karl Landsteiner began studying why some patients died as a result of blood transfusions. He discovered the existence of different human blood types and subsequently classified them as four groups: A, B, AB and O. Type O is known as the universal donor because type O blood can be given to patients with any blood group whereas type AB is known as the universal recipient: patients with type AB blood can receive blood from any blood group. The table shows which group is compatible with which.

Type	Can give to	Can receive from
O	Any blood group	O
AB	AB	Any blood group
A	A and AB	A and O
B	B and AB	B and O

What is the Rhesus factor?

The Rhesus factor (abbreviated as Rh) is an antigen found in the red blood cells of most people and animals. Blood that is described as rhesus positive contains this antigen, whereas rhesus negative blood does not.

The cultural and historical significance of blood

The use of the word 'blood' in the English language shows that, historically, the circulation has had a moral and social importance beyond its biological necessity, signifying family, connection and emotion. 'Blood is thicker than water' means that family duties and connections are stronger than any others. 'Blood money' refers to the compensation paid to the relatives of a murder victim in an attempt to stop them seeking revenge. If you have 'bad blood' you are likely to feel unwell and friends or relatives with 'bad blood' between them do not like each other. The term 'blue blood' comes from the Spanish sangre azul, which was used to describe aristocrats of 'purer' ancestry than those with 'mixed' blood. It is still used today to refer to the nobility and aristocracy.

Since blood has such a strong link to family and emotions it is no surprise that 'cold-blooded' means lacking feeling and 'making one's blood boil' means causing anger.

DISEASES AND DISORDERS

Varicose veins
Venous blood in the lower body has to move uphill in order to return to the heart. Valves prevent the blood flowing backwards but sometimes these valves, especially those in the superficial veins of the legs, no longer work effectively. Consequently the veins become dilated and blood collects in the veins instead of returning to the heart. The veins become distended and knobbly, showing through the skin.

Varicose veins are often caused by:
● heredity
● excessive periods of sitting and standing
● pregnancy
● obesity.

Anaemia
Anaemia is a reduction in the blood's ability to carry oxygen, caused either by a decrease in red blood cells, or the haemoglobin they carry, or both. It may be caused by extensive loss of blood, lack of iron in the diet, the failure of bone marrow to produce the normal level of cells or it may be inherited.

Leukaemia
Leukaemia is a cancer of the blood, caused by over-production of white blood cells.

Septicaemia
Also known as blood poisoning, this is a generalised disease associated with the circulation and multiplication of toxic bacteria in the blood.

Haemophilia
The blood's inability to clot. This is an inherited disease which affects mainly men but which can be carried by women.

Arteriosclerosis
A degenerative disease of the arteries, in which the walls of the vessels harden and lose elasticity. The loss of elasticity causes an increase in blood pressure. This condition mainly affects the elderly.

Atherosclerosis
A build-up of fats, including cholesterol, inside the arteries which causes a narrowing of the artery passage, hardening of the vessel walls and a loss of elasticity.

Blue baby
A baby born with a congenital heart abnormality.

Haemorrhoids
Also known as piles, these are enlarged veins in the rectum or anus which may collapse or contain blood clots.

Phlebitis
Inflammation of a vein. Thrombo-phlebitis is the inflammation of a vein where a blood clot has formed.

Thrombus
A blood clot in the heart or in the blood vessels.

HIV/AIDS
AIDS stands for Acquired Immune Deficiency Syndrome. It is a complex disease caused by the HIV (human immuno-deficiency) virus. The virus attacks T-lymphocytes, making the immune system incapable of fighting disease. It is transmitted through blood and other body fluids.

High blood pressure

Also known as hypertension, this is blood pressure which consistently remains above the normal level.

Low blood pressure

Also known as hypotension, this is blood pressure which consistently remains below the normal level.

High cholesterol

High cholesterol is an excessive build-up of a fatty substance called cholesterol, which can cause a reduction in arterial capacity (atherosclerosis – see previous page) and thus high blood pressure.

Diabetes

A condition of the pancreas and the blood. Insulin (a substance produced in the pancreas) helps the body burn glucose for energy. If there is not enough insulin the blood contains too much sugar, fat is burnt instead and this is dangerous.

Hepatitis A B C

Inflammations of the liver, caused by viruses, toxic substances or immunological abnormalities. Type A is spread by fecally contaminated food. Types B and C are transmitted by infected body fluids including blood. Contagious.

Coronary thrombosis

A blood clot in the coronary artery.

Stress

Stress can be defined as any factor which affects mental or physical health. When a person is stressed, the heart beats faster, thus pumping blood more quickly. Excessive and unresolved stress can lead to high blood pressure, coronary thrombosis and heart attacks.

Interrelationships

Circulatory system links to:

Respiratory: carries oxygen to every cell and system of the body (internal respiration); removes waste gas from the body through diffusion between capillary/alveoli (external respiration).

Lymphatic: linked to the lymphatic system at tissue level – the circulatory system transports some waste products away from the tissues (mainly carbon dioxide) and any additional waste products are carried away by the lymphatic system. The circulatory and lymphatic systems also work together to protect the body (immunity). The lymphatic system empties back into the blood system.

Endocrine: hormones carried in blood to various target organs

Digestive: nutrients broken down in the digestive process are transported by blood from the small intestines to the liver then around the body

Muscular: blood transports glucose for energy conversion to the muscles.

Urinary: blood passes through the kidneys for purification of toxins

Skeletal: erythrocytes and leucocytes are manufactured in the bone marrow of long bones

Skin: circulation transports oxygen and nutrition to skin, hair and nails.

SUMMARY

- *Blood is the body's fuel, delivered by the circulatory system: it carries nutrients and oxygen to the body and collects waste and carbon dioxide from it*
- *The heart is the circulatory system's engine: it pumps blood around the body*
- *Arteries and veins are the circulatory system's pipes: they transport arterial blood from the heart (except the pulmonary artery) and venous blood to the heart (except the pulmonary vein).*

The Lymphatic System

A circulatory system as complicated as that of the blood requires support. In the human body this is provided by the lymphatic system.

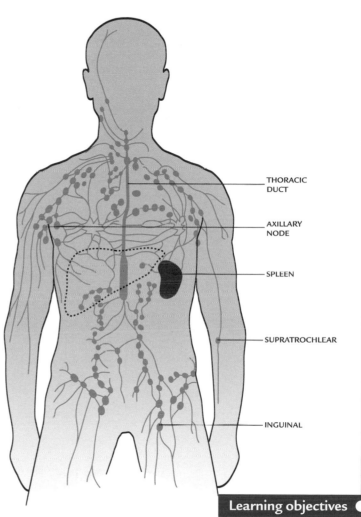

THORACIC DUCT

AXILLARY NODE

SPLEEN

SUPRATROCHLEAR

INGUINAL

OVERVIEW OF THE LYMPHATIC SYSTEM
SHOWING LYMPH NODES AND SPLEEN

In Brief

The lymphatic system is a subsidiary circulation entwined with the blood circulation. It provides a channel through which excess tissue fluid is returned to the bloodstream.

Learning objectives

The target knowledge of this chapter is:
- the structure of the lymphatic system
- the function of the lymphatic system
- the position of the main lymph nodes and ducts in the body
- the connection between blood and lymph.
- diseases and disorders of the lymphatic system.

STRUCTURE AND FUNCTION

What is the lymphatic system?

In order to understand the lymphatic system it is necessary to understand what happens in the circulatory system at tissue level. Blood travels to and from the tissues delivering nutrients and removing waste. Whole blood never leaves the capillaries, only its 'passengers' (i.e. oxygen, food, water) do and they are carried by a derivative of blood plasma called tissue, or interstitial fluid. This fluid circulates throughout the tissues, delivering food, oxygen and water to the cells and collecting carbon dioxide and other waste. However, when it has finished its work and needs to return to the capillaries, not all of it can pass through the capillary walls because the pressure inside the capillaries is too high. The fluid that is left is picked up by a different set of capillaries, called the lymphatic capillaries. They have larger pores in their walls than blood capillaries

and the pressure inside them is lower. Thus, excess tissue fluid, substances made of large molecules, fragments of damaged cells and foreign matter such as micro-organisms drain away into them. The fluid, known as lymph, is filtered by the lymph nodes then collected by the lymphatic ducts before entering the right and left subclavian veins and returning to the bloodstream.

What is the structure of the lymphatic system?

The lymphatic system consists of lymphatic capillaries, lymphatic vessels, lymph nodes and lymphatic ducts. The fluid in lymphatic capillaries and vessels is called lymph.

What does it distribute and collect?

Lymph, a fluid similar to blood plasma.

Structure: contains waste materials as well as leucocytes and lymphocytes (in order to ingest bacteria and cell debris) but no erythrocytes.

Function: transports excess waste (that blood cannot carry) away from tissues; adds extra leucocytes and lymphocytes to the blood.

How does lymph move?

Several factors help to circulate lymph –

● the contraction of skeletal muscles collapses the vessels and because there are valves present, lymph is directed towards the upper part of the body
● a slight oncoming pressure from the tissue fluids
● movement of the lymph towards the thorax during inspiration
● suction: negative pressure helps to pull the lymph upwards into the lymphatic ducts, where lymph collects before

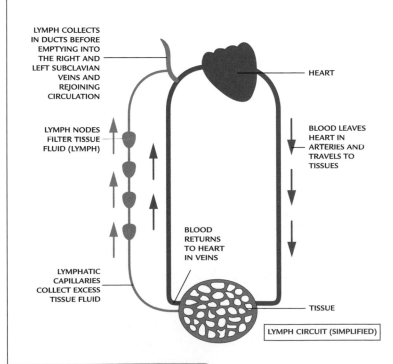

LYMPH COLLECTS IN DUCTS BEFORE EMPTYING INTO THE RIGHT AND LEFT SUBCLAVIAN VEINS AND REJOINING CIRCULATION

LYMPH NODES FILTER TISSUE FLUID (LYMPH)

LYMPHATIC CAPILLARIES COLLECT EXCESS TISSUE FLUID

HEART

BLOOD LEAVES HEART IN ARTERIES AND TRAVELS TO TISSUES

BLOOD RETURNS TO HEART IN VEINS

TISSUE

LYMPH CIRCUIT (SIMPLIFIED)

being recirculated. These ducts empty into the subclavian veins which, because they are close to the heart, have negative pressure in them. This pressure pulls on the ducts and thus on the lymph vessels connected to them.

Any obstruction of the lymphatic flow results in oedema, the swelling of tissues due to the collection of excess fluid.

What are lymphatic capillaries?

The vessels which work with blood to collect excess tissue fluid. Lymphatic capillaries eventually unite to form lymphatic vessels.

Structure: fine, blind-ended permeable tubes, composed of a single layer of endothelial cells. They occur in all spaces between tissues, except in the central nervous system.

Function: carry excess tissue fluid away from tissue space.

What are lymphatic vessels?

These are vessels which transport lymph around the lymphatic system.

Structure: thin-walled, collapsible vessels similar to veins but carrying lymph not venous blood. They have valves (semi-lunar) to keep the lymph moving centripetally (in the direction of the heart) and prevent back flow. Consisting of a double layer of lining membrane, these valves give the vessels a knotted or beaded appearance. They have three layers:
- an outer layer of fibrous tissue
- a middle layer of muscular and elastic tissue
- an inner layer of endothelial cells.

Function: lymphatic vessels collect lymph from the lymphatic capillaries and then convey lymph towards the heart. Many lymph vessels run into the subcutaneous tissue (beneath the dermis) and all the lymphatic vessels pass through one or more lymphatic nodes.

WHAT IS THE CONNECTION BETWEEN BLOOD AND LYMPH?

The lymphatic system is a subsidiary circulation, helping the blood circulation to carry out its functions. It removes excess fluid from tissues and carries large particles that cannot pass through the smaller pores of the blood capillaries. Lymph nodes and the spleen filter lymph (the name of the fluid in the lymphatic system) and take out the waste materials it contains as well as producing antibodies and lymphocytes which are added to the lymph to be transported to the blood.

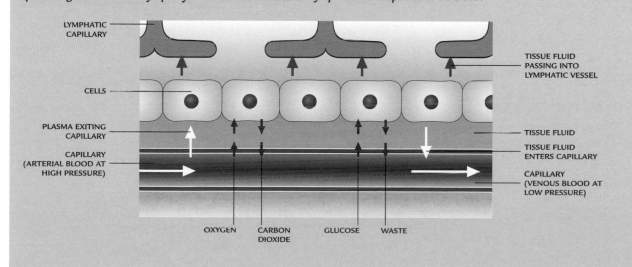

What are lymph nodes?

All the small and medium-sized lymph vessels open into lymph nodes, which are strategically placed throughout the body. An afferent vessel transports lymph to the node and an efferent vessel transports the filtered lymph back to the system.

Structure: each node is made of lymphatic tissue, surrounded by a wall of tough, white fibrous tissue supported by inward strands of fibrous tissue called *trabeculae*. Lymph nodes vary in size.

Functions:

- to filter the lymph, remove and destroy harmful micro-organisms, tumour cells, damaged or dead tissue cells, large protein molecules and toxic substances. This filtering system prevents toxic materials from reaching the bloodstream and causing septicaemia. If this occurs, it can cause the node to swell. In severe cases, this may cause cell destruction and an abscess on the node.
- to produce new lymphocytes and antibodies and add them to the lymph as necessary.
- lymphatic tissue cells within the node may become activated to form antibodies against a particular infection. They may then continue to form antibodies for several years or even a lifetime.

What is lymphatic tissue?

Lymph nodes are made of lymphatic tissue. This contains many types of cells:
- phagocytes – engulf and destroy harmful (pathogenic) waste and bacteria
- cells producing antibodies (lymphocytes)
- cells dividing to form new lymphocytes.

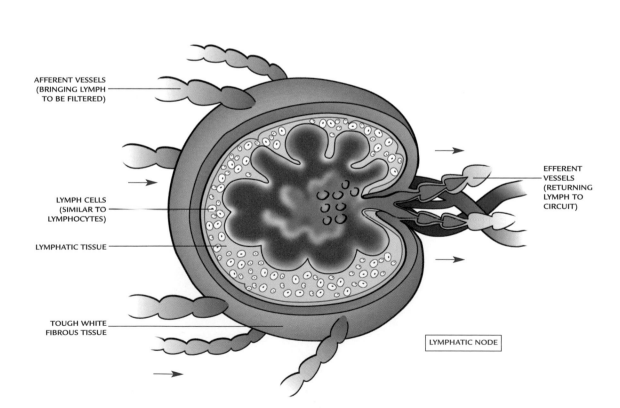

AFFERENT VESSELS (BRINGING LYMPH TO BE FILTERED)

EFFERENT VESSELS (RETURNING LYMPH TO CIRCUIT)

LYMPH CELLS (SIMILAR TO LYMPHOCYTES)

LYMPHATIC TISSUE

TOUGH WHITE FIBROUS TISSUE

LYMPHATIC NODE

What are lymphatic ducts?
All lymph passes into two main lymphatic vessels, or ducts:

1. The right lymphatic duct
This is only 1.5cm long, positioned at the root of the neck and empties into the right subclavian vein to rejoin the circulatory system.
Function: receives all the drained lymph from the right side of the head, chest and neck and from the right arm.

2. The thoracic duct
This is the largest lymphatic vessel. It is 40cm long extending from the second lumbar vertebra to the root of the neck and empties into the subclavian vein to rejoin the circulatory system.
Function: collects and drains lymph from the left side of the head, the neck, both lower limbs, the left side of the trunk and the left arm.

Special areas containing lymphatic tissue (shown by numbers on the diagram)

3. TONSILS
4. THYMUS GLAND (BEHIND STERNUM)
5. PEYER'S PATCHES (WALL OF SMALL INTESTINE)
6. APPENDIX
7. SPLEEN

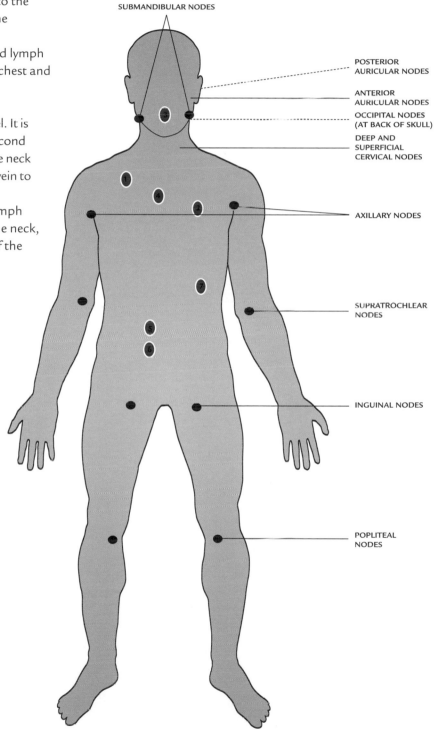

SUBMANDIBULAR NODES

POSTERIOR AURICULAR NODES

ANTERIOR AURICULAR NODES

OCCIPITAL NODES (AT BACK OF SKULL)

DEEP AND SUPERFICIAL CERVICAL NODES

AXILLARY NODES

SUPRATROCHLEAR NODES

INGUINAL NODES

POPLITEAL NODES

Spleen

The spleen is an organ which both produces and destroys cells. It is a non-essential organ and is sometimes removed due to damage after accidents, as other organs can perform the same functions. The spleen lies on the upper left-hand side of the abdomen.

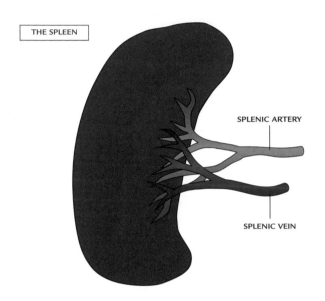

THE SPLEEN

SPLENIC ARTERY

SPLENIC VEIN

Structure: the spleen has an outer capsule of fibrous tissue extending into a network of fibrous strands called trabeculae. This network supports the splenic pulp which consists of several different types of cells.

Functions:
- forms new lymphocytes
- destroys thrombocytes and erythrocytes
- helps to remove foreign particles from the circulation
- helps to fight infection, becoming enlarged in certain diseases, e.g. malaria and typhoid fever
- acts as a blood reservoir. Blood sinuses within the spleen normally hold a large amount of blood which is pushed into general circulation if the spleen contracts. Contraction usually occurs two or three times a minute, but in cases of shock or even during exercise, the spleen may contract faster and for a longer period to help maintain pressure in the circulation.

DISEASES

Hodgkin's disease
Cancer of the lymphatic tissue.

Interrelationships
Lymphatic system links to:
Circulatory: transports excess waste and toxins, which the circulatory system cannot cope with, away from the cells and tissues. Also works closely with the circulatory system to strengthen the body's immunity.
Digestive: lymphatic vessels in the small intestines (inside the lacteal of the ileum) help with the absorption of fats during digestion. These are then transported around the body in the circulatory system and distributed to cells to be used as energy.
Muscular: lactic acid formed when over-exercising muscles, or from tension and general fatigue in the muscular system, are drained away in the lymphatic system.

SUMMARY
- *Provides a channel for transporting excess tissue fluid away from tissues and back to the blood circulation.*
- *Collects and transports lymph from tissue cells.*
- *Nodes filter lymph of harmful materials before returning it to the blood circulation.*
- *Produces new lymphocytes.*
- *Produces antibodies.*
- *Lymphatic capillaries in the lining of the small intestine assist in the absorption of fat droplets.*

The Nervous System

The nervous system is a communication and instruction network. It is composed of the brain, spinal cord and nerves.

In Brief

The nervous system informs the brain about what is happening and thus protects the body. There are two parts: the central nervous system and the peripheral nervous system. The brain is the main unit and it is connected to the rest of the body by nerve cells which function as messengers, carrying information to, and instructions from the brain. They report back on pain, sensation and danger so that the body can respond and remain in what is known as homeostasis: a stable, physiological state.

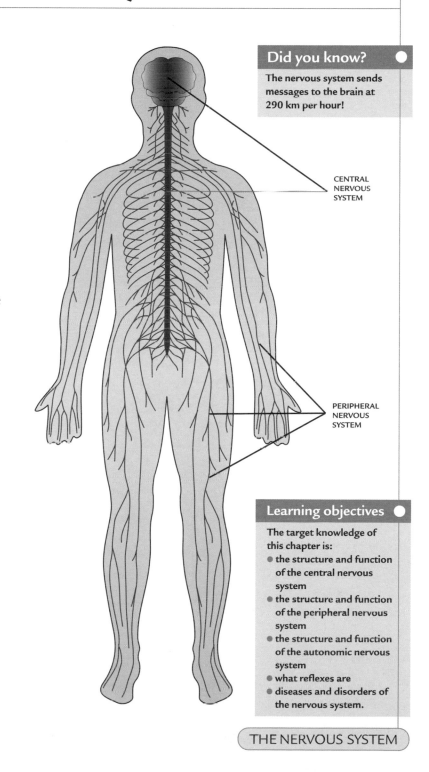

Did you know?

The nervous system sends messages to the brain at 290 km per hour!

CENTRAL NERVOUS SYSTEM

PERIPHERAL NERVOUS SYSTEM

Learning objectives

The target knowledge of this chapter is:
- the structure and function of the central nervous system
- the structure and function of the peripheral nervous system
- the structure and function of the autonomic nervous system
- what reflexes are
- diseases and disorders of the nervous system.

STRUCTURE

What is the nervous system made of?

Nervous tissue which is composed of:

- nerve cells, known as neurones, with attached fibres
- neuroglia, a connective tissue which supports the neurones; though only found in the nervous system, neuroglia does not transmit nerve impulses.

What is a nerve cell?

Nerve cells are the basic unit of the system on which everything else is built. Like all cells, they have a membrane containing a nucleus and a cytoplasm but they have a particular shape: long and narrow. Some are very long (up to a metre). Nerve cells are easily damaged by toxins and lack of oxygen. Unlike other cells in the body, they are not usually replaced when they die, however, current research suggests that some may have the ability to regenerate. The main parts of a nerve cell are:

- **cell body**: the centre of the neurone, with a nucleus and cytoplasm
- **dendrites**: nerve fibres, like branches, which transmit nerve impulses to the cell body; most neurones have several dendrites
- **axon**: a long single nerve fibre, which transmits nerve impulses away from the cell body; neurones generally have only one axon
- **myelin sheath**: made of a white, fatty substance, this sheath covers the axon. It insulates the axon, protects it from pressure and helps speed up nerve conduction (the speed at which messages are transmitted)
- **neurilemma**: a fine, delicate membrane which surrounds axons and helps regenerate nerve cells; only found in peripheral nerves and not in the brain or spinal cord
- **nodes of Ranvier**: these are compressed points in the myelin sheath along the nerve. They speed up the passage of nerve impulses along the fibre
- **end feet/axon terminals**: the ends of the fibrils (tiny fibres) that make the axon are expanded and called end feet or axon terminals. They pass on the nerve impulse to the dendrites of the next neurone
- **synapse**: the point where one neurone meets another. A chemical messenger fills the gap between one neurone and the next, and enables the impulse to be transmitted

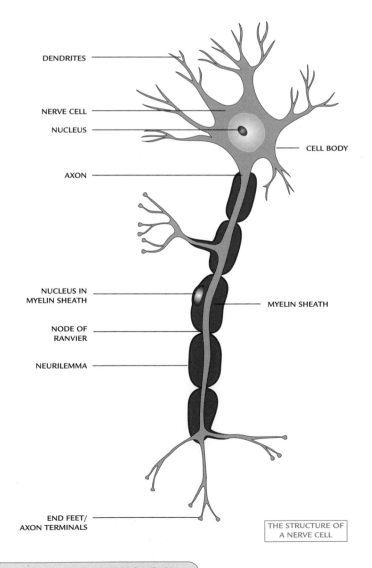

DENDRITES

NERVE CELL

NUCLEUS

AXON

CELL BODY

NUCLEUS IN
MYELIN SHEATH

MYELIN SHEATH

NODE OF
RANVIER

NEURILEMMA

END FEET/
AXON TERMINALS

THE STRUCTURE OF
A NERVE CELL

FUNCTION

77

What does a nerve cell do?
Nerve cells act as links in a chain, like relay runners, each one passing the 'baton' (information or instruction) to the next until it reaches the brain or the part of the body in question. The axon of one cell is close to the dendrite of the next but they don't actually touch. The 'baton' of nerve impulses jumps across the gap via neuro-transmitters, chemicals released by the nerve endings.

Collective function
Individual neurones have the same function throughout the body, to transmit information, but collectively they make up five different types of nerves and nervous tissue which have specific functions:
- **motor or efferent nerves**: carry impulses from the brain or spinal cord to the muscles which then act on the information/instruction, producing movement or constricting a vessel. Motor nerves only transmit to glandular and muscular tissue.
- **sensory or afferent nerves**: carry impulses from all parts of the body to the brain.
- **mixed**: carry both motor and sensory nerve fibres. Mixed nerves are only present in the spinal nerves.
- **white matter**: on the inside of the brain and the outside of the spinal cord; this is made of bundles of myelinated nerve fibres (i.e. with a sheath).
- **grey matter**: on the outside of the brain and inside of the spinal cord – this is made of cell bodies and unmyelinated axons and dendrites.

What is a nerve impulse?
Nerve cells transmit and receive impulses throughout the body. Nerve impulses do not continually run along each nerve. Impulses are created in response to particular stimuli, like changes in temperature, pressure or chemicals. These impulses are caused by chemical changes in the cell body. Chemical compounds generate electrical charges. Inside the cell there are potassium ions, which are positively charged, and the tissue fluid outside the cell contains sodium ions which are also positively charged. However, the membrane is more permeable to potassium than to sodium with the result that the outside of the cell has more positive charge than the inside. When there is a change of temperature or pressure, or a chemical reaction a section of the nerve membrane becomes permeable to sodium and the positively charged ions rush in, leaving the outside of the membrane negative. This reversal of polarity causes an electrical reaction which stimulates a change in the next section of membrane. The reaction continues the length of the nerve cell and this creates the impulse.

Useful Tip
How do you remember which are afferent and which are efferent nerves? Efferent exit the brain, afferent arrive in the brain.

How do nerve cells communicate?
Nerve impulses only travel in one direction. So the movement of nerve impulses in a single neurone is as follows: the impulse crosses the synapse from the end feet of cell A into the dendrites of cell B. The impulse travels from the dendrites to the cell body and then out again along the axon to cell B's end feet. It then jumps across the synapse, helped by the chemical messengers. This process continues until the impulse reaches either the brain or the muscle/organ concerned.

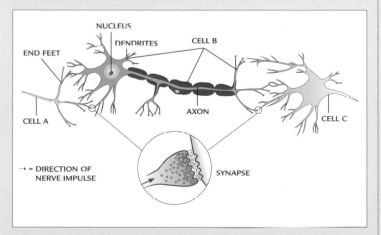

You now know the structure and function of nerve cells and what a nerve impulse is. The next section explains different systems formed by nerve cells.

THE NERVOUS SYSTEM

CENTRAL NERVOUS SYSTEM

There are two parts to the nervous system in the human body:
- central nervous system, consisting of the brain and spinal cord, both covered by meninges.
- peripheral nervous system, consisting of the cranial and spinal nerves and the autonomic nervous system which supplies nerves to all the body's internal organs.

The brain

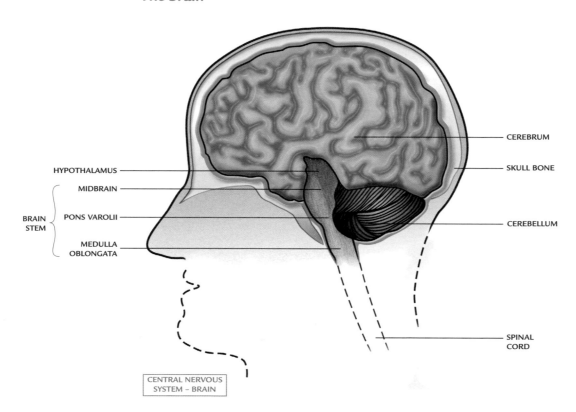

HYPOTHALAMUS
MIDBRAIN
PONS VAROLII
MEDULLA OBLONGATA
BRAIN STEM

CEREBRUM
SKULL BONE
CEREBELLUM
SPINAL CORD

CENTRAL NERVOUS SYSTEM – BRAIN

The brain is the organ that fills the cranium (skull). It stops developing in the 15th year of life. It is the main mass exercising control over the body and mind and it has three different sections:
- the cerebrum (also known as cerebral hemispheres)
- the cerebellum
- the brain stem.

The cerebrum
Structure: this is the largest part of the brain and is divided into two cerebral hemispheres, one on the right and one on the left. The outer layer is made of folds of grey matter (i.e. cell bodies). The folds increase the brain's surface area and thus the number of cell bodies. Inside the grey matter is white matter (i.e. nerve fibres). These fibres connect different parts of the brain together.

Functions:
- controlling voluntary movement (i.e. the movements we choose to make)
- interpreting and perceiving conscious sensations like pain, heat and cold
- controlling mental activity, like memory, intelligence and reasoning.

The cerebellum

Structure: the cerebellum is also known as the 'small brain'. Positioned in the posterior cranial fossa, behind the pons Varolii, below the cerebrum and over the medulla oblongata, it also consists of two hemispheres, grey matter on the surface and white matter within.

Functions:
- co-ordinating muscular activity, making sure movements are smooth and precise (damage to the cerebellum results in clumsy, uncoordinated movements).
- subconsciously controlling and maintaining muscle tone and posture.
- maintaining balance and equilibrium of body.

The brain stem

The brain stem consists of three parts, the midbrain, pons Varolii and the medulla oblongata.

Midbrain

Structure: lies between cerebrum and cerebellum and above the pons Varolii. It is about 2cm long and consists of nerve cells and fibres.

Function: the relay station of the brain, transmitting messages to and from the spinal cord, the cerebrum and the cerebellum.

Pons Varolii

Structure: situated in front of the cerebellum, below the midbrain and above the medulla oblongata. It consists of nerve fibres, which bridge (hence pons, which means bridge in Latin) the gap between the two hemispheres of the cerebellum.

Function: like the midbrain, transmits messages to and from the spinal cord and cerebrum.

Medulla oblongata

Structure: lowest part of the brain stem, situated above the spinal cord and below the pons Varolii. Its construction is different from the cerebrum and cerebellum with white matter on the surface and grey matter in the centre. It is known as a vital centre because it controls the actions of the heart and lungs (respectively the centres of the vascular and respiratory systems). It has four centres.

Functions:
- cardiac centre: controls rate and force of heart contraction
- respiratory centre: controls rate and depth of breathing
- vasomotor centre: controls constriction and dilation of blood vessels
- reflex centre: responds to irritants thus controls vomiting, coughing, sneezing and swallowing.

Hypothalamus

Structure: situated at the base of the midbrain, immediately above the pituitary gland.

Function: helps with the regulation of body temperature, water balance and metabolism. Centre for drives and emotions such as thirst, appetite, sex, pain and pleasure. It also regulates the pituitary gland. It secretes oxytocin and ADH for storage in the posterior pituitary.

The spinal cord

The spinal cord is the other main part of the central nervous system.

Structure: the spinal cord extends from the medulla oblongata through the spinal vertebrae ending at the first lumbar vertebra. It consists of white matter on the surface and grey matter inside and gives off 31 pairs of spinal nerves as well as part of one cranial nerve along its length.

Function: the spinal cord carries motor and sensory nerve fibres along its length, sending messages about feeling and movement to and from the body and brain.

Other important parts of the central nervous system

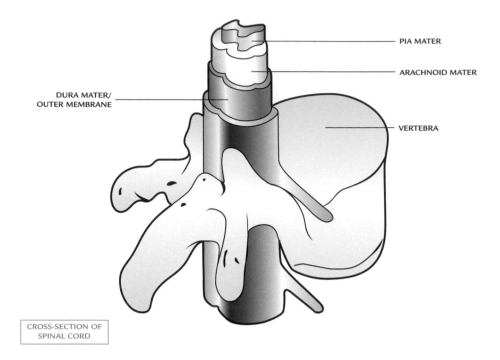

PIA MATER

ARACHNOID MATER

DURA MATER/
OUTER MEMBRANE

VERTEBRA

CROSS-SECTION OF
SPINAL CORD

The meninges
The meninges are membranes which protect the whole of the central nervous system. There are three different layers –
- **dura mater, or outer membrane**: a double layer of tough, fibrous membrane: the outer layer forms the periosteum ('skin') of the skull while the inner layer, the first protective covering of the brain, continues as the spinal dura mater as far down as the sacrum.
- **arachnoid mater**: a delicate membrane positioned immediately under the dura and above the pia mater. It merges with the dura mater and thus covers the spinal cord as far as the sacrum. It connects to the sub-arachnoid space, situated between the arachnoid mater and the pia mater and is filled with cerebrospinal fluid (see below).
- **pia mater**: a thin, vascular membrane which closely covers the brain, dipping into the various surface folds of the cerebrum and cerebellum, and

continues along the length of the spinal cord. It supplies blood to the brain and spinal cord.

Ventricles and cerebrospinal fluid
There are four cavities inside the brain called ventricles, all containing cerebrospinal fluid. Two of these ventricles lie laterally within the cerebrum, a third lies deep inside the brain whereas the fourth, also deep inside the brain, opens into the sub-arachnoid space.

Cerebrospinal fluid
Structure: this is clear, colourless fluid, formed in special cells within choroid plexuses that are situated in the lining of the ventricles. It resembles blood plasma in composition, containing protein, glucose, salts, and other substances. It is secreted into the ventricles from where it circulates around the whole brain and spinal cord and is then reabsorbed into the venous sinuses of the body through

the arachnoid mater.

Functions:
- protects the brain and spinal cord, forming a cushion between the bony cavities and the nerves and acting as a shock absorber
- keeps the pressure around the brain and spinal cord constant
- transports nutrients and removes waste and toxic substances.

You now know the structure and functions of all the main parts of the central nervous system. The next section explains the peripheral and autonomic nervous systems.

THE PERIPHERAL NERVOUS SYSTEM

What is the peripheral nervous system?

The peripheral nervous system concerns all the nervous system outside the central nervous system and contains motor and sensory nerves which transmit information to and from the body and brain. It consists of 12 pairs of cranial nerves, 31 pairs of spinal nerves and the autonomic nervous system.

Cranial nerves

These nerves begin and end within the brain. They include the olfactory nerve, (the nerve of smell) and the optic nerve (the nerve of sight). The 12 pairs include motor, sensory and mixed nerves.

Spinal nerves

These pairs of nerves are divided into plexuses (groups of nerves which branch out to supply different parts of the body) named after the vertebrae to which they are connected:
- cervical: eight pairs
- thoracic: twelve pairs
- lumbar: five pairs
- sacral: five pairs
- coccygeal: one pair.

The lumbar, sacral and coccygeal nerves leave the spinal cord at the level of the first lumbar vertebra and extend downwards, forming a bundle of nerves known as the cauda equina (which means horse's tail in Latin, a reference to what the bundle looks like). These nerves group into plexuses with other adjacent nerves.

The cervical plexus

This contains the first four cervical nerves and supplies the muscles of the neck, shoulder and skin and the phrenic nerve, which sends nerve impulses to the diaphragm telling it to contract.

The brachial plexus

This group includes the lower four cervical nerves and the first thoracic nerve. It branches out to supply the muscles from the base of the neck to the fingertips and skin.

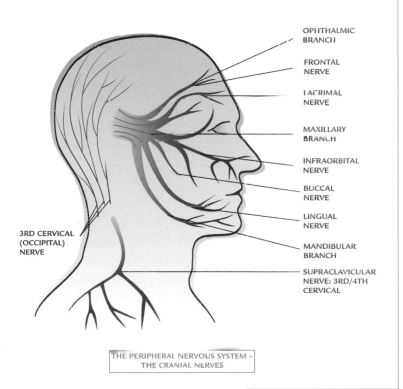

3RD CERVICAL (OCCIPITAL) NERVE

OPHTHALMIC BRANCH
FRONTAL NERVE
LACRIMAL NERVE
MAXILLARY BRANCH
INFRAORBITAL NERVE
BUCCAL NERVE
LINGUAL NERVE
MANDIBULAR BRANCH
SUPRACLAVICULAR NERVE: 3RD/4TH CERVICAL

THE PERIPHERAL NERVOUS SYSTEM – THE CRANIAL NERVES

THE NERVOUS SYSTEM

The thoracic (intercostal) nerves

The thoracic nerves supply the chest muscles and the main part of the abdominal wall.

The lumbar plexus

This group includes the first three lumbar nerves and part of the fourth. It supplies the skin and muscles of the lower abdomen, thighs and groin.

The sacral plexus

This includes the fourth and fifth lumbar nerves and first four sacral nerves. It supplies the muscles and skin of the pelvic area and the hamstrings, dividing at mid-femur into the tibial nerve and common peroneal. It includes the sciatic nerve, the largest nerve in the body.

The coccygeal plexus

The coccygeal group forms a second small plexus on the back of the pelvic cavity, supplying the muscles and skin of the pelvic area such as the external sphincter of the anus, tissues of the perineum and the external genitalia.

THE AUTONOMIC NERVOUS SYSTEM

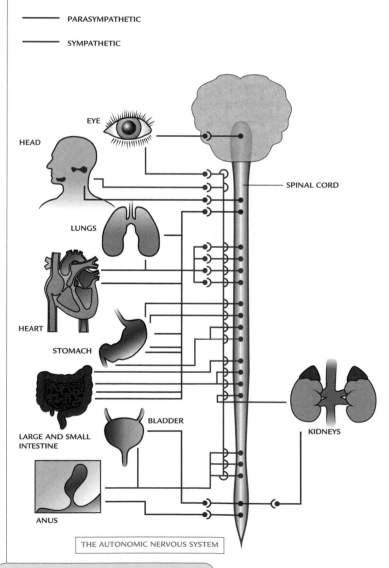

——— PARASYMPATHETIC

——— SYMPATHETIC

EYE
HEAD
LUNGS
HEART
STOMACH
LARGE AND SMALL INTESTINE
BLADDER
ANUS
SPINAL CORD
KIDNEYS

THE AUTONOMIC NERVOUS SYSTEM

What is the autonomic nervous system?

The autonomic nervous system supplies nerves to all the internal organs of the body and to the blood vessels. It regulates events which are autonomic. It is controlled by the hypothalamus and its actions are thus not controlled by the brain or will, but are completely reflex and involuntary. Thus the brain does not know, and nor do we, when the actions happen. The system is divided into two parts:
● sympathetic
● parasympathetic.

Every organ in the body has a sympathetic and parasympathetic nerve supply.

Sympathetic

Structure: consists of ganglia (a collection of nerve cells) which are situated in front of the vertebral column and travel the length of the body from the thoracic to the lumbar region.

Functions:
● stimulates action of organ. Releases noradrenaline which prepares the body for excitement and stress (fight or flight syndrome).

- accelerates action of heart, increasing rate and force of contraction.
- causes dilation (relaxation) of arteries, increasing blood supply to the heart muscles.
- causes dilation of blood vessels supplying skeletal muscles, increasing the nourishing and waste removal processes thus enabling the muscle to work better.
- causes sustained contraction of the spleen, thus increasing volume of blood circulating.
- raises blood pressure by constricting small arteries and arterioles that supply the skin.
- constricts blood vessels in secretory glands of digestive system, restricting flow of digestive juices.

Parasympathetic

Structure: consists of the vagus, oculomotor, facial and glossopharyngeal nerves, which branch off to all the organs in chest and abdomen.

Functions:
- slows down action of organ. Stimulates the opposite reaction in organs to that produced by sympathetic nerves.
- releases acetylcholine, a neurotransmitter.
- slows action of heart, reducing rate and force of contraction.
- constricts flow of blood to heart muscles.

What are reflexes?

A reflex is the automatic (i.e. not controlled by the brain) movement produced by a sensory stimulus. It is instant and involuntary e.g. a finger touching boiling hot water will immediately move away.

Several structures are involved in the production of a reflex and together they constitute the 'reflex arc':
- a sense organ, like the skin or the nerve endings in muscles, tendons or organs
- a sensory nerve travelling from the sensory organ via the periphery nerve to the spinal cord
- the spinal cord
- a motor nerve starting in the spinal cord and travelling via the periphery nerve to the motor organ.

Function: reflexes are mostly protective and designed to stimulate the quickest motor responses (movements) possible. There are also reflexes which are automatic and do not require supervision, like the secretion of gastric juices when food reaches the stomach.

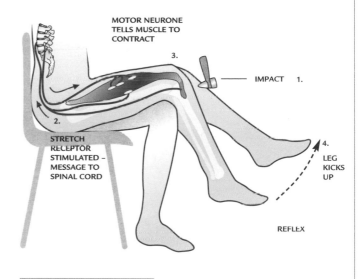

MOTOR NEURONE TELLS MUSCLE TO CONTRACT

3.

IMPACT 1.

2.

STRETCH RECEPTOR STIMULATED – MESSAGE TO SPINAL CORD

4.

LEG KICKS UP

REFLEX

EXAMPLE OF A REFLEX ACTION

You now know the structure and function of all three different parts of the nervous system. The final section explains diseases and disorders of the systems.

DISEASES AND DISORDERS

Neuritis
Inflammation of a nerve, caused by infection, injury, poison, etc.
Effect: pain along the nerve's length and/or loss of use of the structures supplied by the nerve.

Bell's palsy
Facial paralysis, caused by injury to or infection of the facial nerve which subsequently becomes inflamed.

Neuralgia
Bouts of burning or stabbing pain, along the course of one or more nerves due to various causes.

Sciatica
Pain down the back and outside of the thigh, leg and foot, often caused by degeneration of intervertebral disc.

Parkinson's disease
Progressive disease caused by damage to basal ganglia of the brain and resulting in loss of dopamine (neuro-transmitter).
Effect: causes tremor and rigidity in muscles, as well as difficulty and slowness with voluntary movement.

Multiple sclerosis
(also known as disseminated sclerosis)
Loss of the protective myelin sheath from nerve fibres in the central nervous system.
Effect: causes muscular weakness, loss of muscular coordination, problems with skin sensation, speech and vision.

Cerebral palsy
Damage to the brain, caused during birth or resulting from a pre-natal defect.
Effect: affects motor system control.

Motor neurone disease
A rare progressive disorder, in which the motor neurones in the body gradually deteriorate structurally and functionally.

Myalgic encephalomelitis (ME)
Known as post-viral fatigue. This disease is both difficult to diagnose and describe because the causes and effects differ. Symptoms include exhaustion, general aches and pains, headaches and dizziness.

Stress
Stress is any factor that affects mental or physical well-being. Emotions such as anxiety, fear and other negative feelings can affect the nervous system causing increased heart rate, breathing difficulties, sleep disturbances and stomach problems. All of these physical effects are caused by the nervous system over-working in response to stress.

Interrelationships
Nervous system links to:
All systems: nerves from the central nervous system control and receive information from every body system.
Muscular: muscles require a nerve impulse to contract.
Skeletal: muscle contraction (caused by nerve impulses) produces movement in the skeleton.
Circulatory: nerves control the heart rate.
Respiratory: nerves control the process of respiration.
Endocrine: works closely with the endocrine system to maintain homeostasis — balance in the body.
Skin: the skin contains a variety of nerve endings, at different levels in the layers.

SUMMARY

The nervous system:
- *has two parts, the central and peripheral (including autonomic) nervous systems*
- *informs and warns the body of environmental changes, sensations, pain and danger and initiates responses to stimuli.*

The Endocrine System

The endocrine system is one of the body's communication systems. It uses hormones to tell the body what to do.

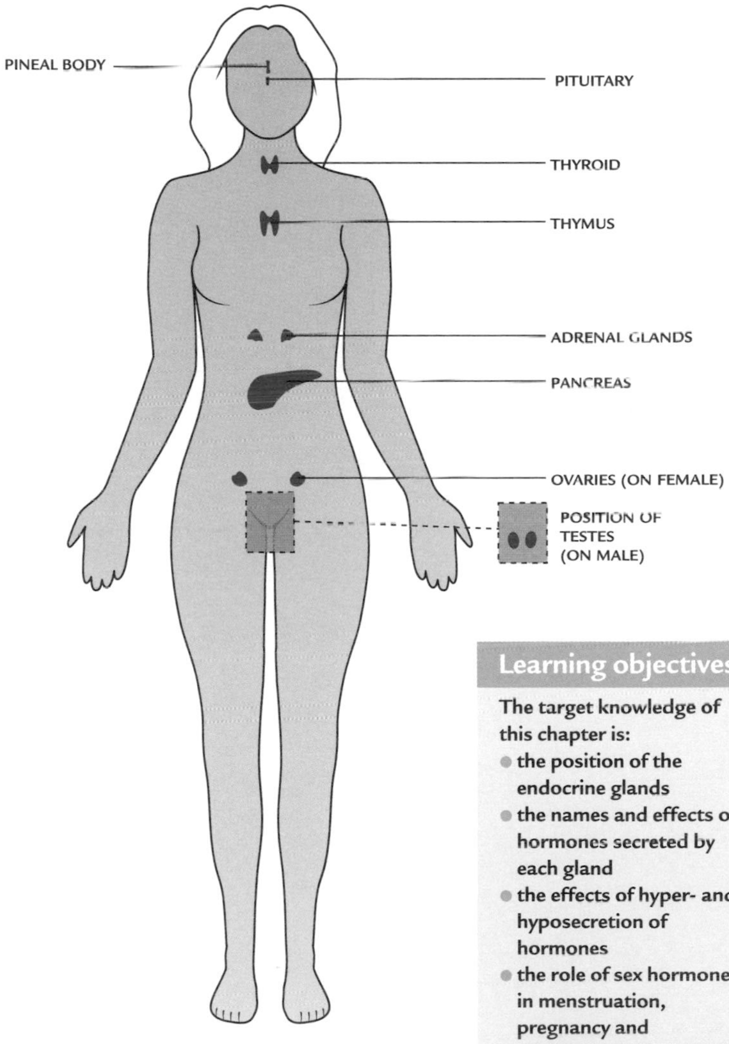

PINEAL BODY

PITUITARY

THYROID

THYMUS

ADRENAL GLANDS

PANCREAS

OVARIES (ON FEMALE)

POSITION OF TESTES (ON MALE)

MAIN ENDOCRINE GLANDS OF THE BODY (SHOWN ON FEMALE)

In Brief

The endocrine system is composed of ductless glands which produce hormones, the body's chemical messengers. Hormones control and affect many body functions and organs, as well as behaviour. Each gland produces specific hormones. The function of the endocrine system is closely linked to that of the nervous system.

Learning objectives ●

The target knowledge of this chapter is:
● the position of the endocrine glands
● the names and effects of hormones secreted by each gland
● the effects of hyper- and hyposecretion of hormones
● the role of sex hormones in menstruation, pregnancy and menopause
● the different stages of the menstrual cycle
● diseases and disorders of the endocrine system.

STRUCTURE AND FUNCTION

What is a hormone?

A hormone is a chemical messenger, which is secreted directly into the blood by a particular gland. Some hormones, such as insulin, are made of protein, but others are steroids (adreno-corticoid hormones), glycoproteins (FSH, LH, TSH), and derivatives of single amino acids, (T4, T3). Hormones are produced in the gland and are then transported to the area/organ they control or affect.

What is an endocrine gland?

A ductless gland which produces hormones. Ductless means that there is no separate canal or tube to transport the hormones to the blood. Hormones travel straight into the bloodstream from the gland.

What do hormones and the endocrine system do?

They affect the behaviour and function of different areas of the body and of the body overall, e.g. hormones are responsible for correct growth, changes during puberty, the menstrual cycle, pregnancy, the menopause, responses to stress and danger and the proper functioning of the kidneys and digestive system.

The main glands of the body

The diagram opposite displays the main endocrine glands of the body and lists the hormones secreted. The following section explains the function and malfunction of each hormone. If too much of a hormone is produced it is known as hypersecretion; too little is known as hyposecretion.

You now know what an endocrine gland is, what a hormone is and what they do. The following section explains all the main endocrine glands, the hormones they secrete, their functions and malfunctions.

THE GLANDS AND THEIR HORMONES

Pituitary

Location: Situated at the base of the brain, closely connected to the hypothalamus; has two hormone-secreting lobes, the anterior and posterior.

Anterior lobe hormones

● **Human growth hormone (HGH)**
Function: regulates height and growth; main controller along with genes of final height of a person
Malfunctions: hypersecretion causes gigantism or acromegaly; hyposecretion causes dwarfism.

● **Melanocyte-stimulating hormone (MSH)**
Function: stimulates production of melanin in basal layer of the skin.

● **Thyrotrophin (TSH)**
Function: controls thyroid gland
Malfunctions: *see thyroid gland.*

● **Adrenocorticotrophin (ACTH)**
Function: controls adrenal cortex
Malfunction: *see adrenal cortex.*

● **Prolactin or lactogenic hormone (LTH)**
Function: production of milk during lactation.

● **Gonadotrophins** *(gonad/sex organ hormones)*
Function: control sexual development and organs (ovaries and testes)

● *Follicle-stimulating hormone (FSH)*
Function: stimulates ovaries to produce oestrogen and to ovulate in women and stimulates sperm production in men.

● *Luteinising hormone (LH)*
Function: stimulates ovaries to produce the corpus luteum from ruptured follicle and produce progesterone.

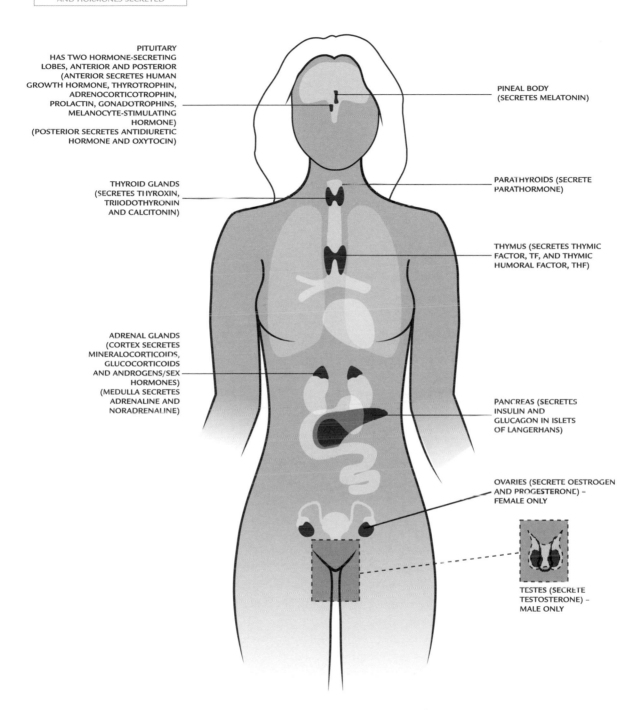

PITUITARY
HAS TWO HORMONE-SECRETING
LOBES, ANTERIOR AND POSTERIOR
(ANTERIOR SECRETES HUMAN
GROWTH HORMONE, THYROTROPHIN,
ADRENOCORTICOTROPHIN,
PROLACTIN, GONADOTROPHINS,
MELANOCYTE-STIMULATING
HORMONE)
(POSTERIOR SECRETES ANTIDIURETIC
HORMONE AND OXYTOCIN)

PINEAL BODY
(SECRETES MELATONIN)

THYROID GLANDS
(SECRETES THYROXIN,
TRIIODOTHYRONIN
AND CALCITONIN)

PARATHYROIDS (SECRETE
PARATHORMONE)

THYMUS (SECRETES THYMIC
FACTOR, TF, AND THYMIC
HUMORAL FACTOR, THF)

ADRENAL GLANDS
(CORTEX SECRETES
MINERALOCORTICOIDS,
GLUCOCORTICOIDS
AND ANDROGENS/SEX
HORMONES)
(MEDULLA SECRETES
ADRENALINE AND
NORADRENALINE)

PANCREAS (SECRETES
INSULIN AND
GLUCAGON IN ISLETS
OF LANGERHANS)

OVARIES (SECRETE OESTROGEN
AND PROGESTERONE) –
FEMALE ONLY

TESTES (SECRETE
TESTOSTERONE) –
MALE ONLY

You now know the location of all the main endocrine glands in the body and the names of the hormones they secrete. The following table explains the functions and malfunctions of the glands and hormones.

THE ENDOCRINE SYSTEM

● *Interstitial cell-stimulating hormone (ICSH)/ luteinising hormone in men*
Function: stimulates sperm production and secretion of testosterone.
Malfunctions (of gonadotrophin): Polycystic ovarian syndrome
Endometriosis
Fibroids
See also adrenal cortex.

Posterior lobe hormones
● **Antidiuretic hormone (ADH or vasopressin)**
Function: regulation of water absorption in kidneys
Malfunctions: hyposecretion: diabetes insipidus; hypersecretion: oedema (swelling).

● **Oxytocin**
Function: contracts mammary glands when suckling begins, to release milk secreted into ducts; contraction of muscles of uterus to begin childbirth and during it.

Thyroid glands
Location: either side of the neck
Hormones: thyroxin, triiodothyronine and calcitonin produced in response to TSH (from pituitary, anterior lobe).
Functions: stimulate tissue metabolism; maintain BMR (basic metabolic rate).
Malfunctions: hypersecretion known as Graves disease or thyrotoxicosis (hyperthyroidism — increase in metabolic rate, heart rate, anxiety, intolerance of heat plus raised temperature, frequent bowel action); hyposecretion — body systems slow below normal speed, cretinism (at birth) or myxoedema (disorder caused later in life by untreated cretinism), goitre – thyroid enlargement.

● **Calcitonin**
Function: maintenance of calcium and phosphorus balance.
Malfunction: hypersecretion causes lowering of blood calcium level by inhibiting loss of calcium from bone.

Parathyroids
Location: four, two either side behind thyroid
Hormone: parathormone
Functions: maintenance of calcium level in plasma; stimulates calcium reabsorption in kidneys; activates Vitamin D.
Malfunctions: hypersecretion – hyper-parathyroidism. Softened bones and thus spontaneous bone fractures; hyposecretion — hypo-parathyroidism: abnormally low blood calcium levels; tetany (spasms in hands and feet caused by over-contraction in muscles); convulsions (from over-stimulated nerves).

Adrenal glands
Location: one on top of each kidney NB: split into two parts, adrenal cortex and adrenal medulla

Adrenal cortex
Hormones:
● **Mineralocorticoids – aldosterone (steroids)**
Function: regulates salts in body, especially sodium chloride and potassium.
Malfunctions: hypersecretion — kidney failure, high blood pressure, too much potassium in blood causing abnormal heart beat; hyposecretion: Addison's disease; muscular atrophy and weakness; body systems slow down.
● **Glucocorticoids (steroids)**
(cortisol and cortisone)
Functions: produced in response

to ACTH (from pituitary, anterior lobe); metabolises carbohydrates, fats and proteins.
Malfunctions: stunted growth; hypersecretion:Cushing's syndrome; hypertension; moon-shaped face; muscular atrophy; diabetes mellitus;
● **Sex hormones (steroids)**; *female*: oestrogen and progesterone (some normal in male); *male*: testosterone (small amounts secreted in the ovaries in females)
Functions: sexual development and maturity; ovulation; hair growth in pubic and axillary (armpit) areas.
Malfunctions: many, including hirsutism, amenorrhoea (hypersecretion of testosterone in women); muscle atrophy and breast growth (hypersecretion of oestrogen in men); hyposecretion: Addison's disease.

Adrenal medulla
The adrenal medulla functions to support the sympathetic nervous system.
Hormones:
● **Adrenaline and noradrenaline**
Function: often known as the stress hormones, they prepare the body for 'fight or flight' by speeding up heart rate, slowing digestive and urinary systems, increasing blood pressure and blood sugar level. Adrenaline is a powerful vasoconstrictor i.e. it constricts blood vessels in order to increase blood pressure.

Pancreas
(specifically in the islets of Langerhans, specialised cells that form the endocrine part of the pancreas)
Location: behind and slightly below stomach, between duodenum and spleen, connected

to duodenum by pancreatic duct
Hormone: insulin and glucogen
Function: helps glucose enter cells thus regulating blood sugar levels.
Malfunctions: hyposecretion: diabetes mellitus (high blood sugar level and high urine production); fatigue; weight loss; coma; hypersecretion: hypoglycaemia (low blood sugar level) including symptoms of hunger, sweating; in serious cases may lead to coma.

Ovaries

Location: either side of the uterus
Hormones: female sex hormones – oestrogen and progesterone (the testes produce a small amount in males)
Functions: responsible for female sexual characteristics e.g. breast growth, widening of hips, pubic and axillary hair growth.

Malfunctions: hyposecretion of luteinising hormone leads to polycystic ovarian syndrome (known as Stein-Leventhal syndrome); hypersecretion of oestrogen in males can lead to muscle atrophy and breast growth.

Testes

Location: within the scrotum, behind the penis
Hormone: male sex hormone – testosterone (the ovaries produce a small amount in females)
Functions: responsible for male sexual characteristics thus sperm production, changes at puberty — voice breaking, pubic, facial and axillary hair growth, increased muscle mass.
Malfunctions: though a low level of testosterone is normal in females, hypersecretion can lead to virilism, hirsutism and amenorrhoea.

Pineal body

Location: centre of the brain
Hormone: melatonin (derived from serotonin)
Function: controls body rhythms – responds to sunlight
Malfunctions: jet-lagged feeling; depression, SAD – seasonal affective disorder.

Thymus

Location: in the thorax
Hormone: TF and THF, (see diagram on page 87), which appear to promote development of T lymphocytes in the thymus gland
Functions: part of immune system
Malfunction: lowered immunity and/or stress.

You now know the location and function of all the main endocrine glands in the body. The following section explains the role of sex hormones.

THE ROLE OF SEX HORMONES

Puberty

Puberty is the age at which the internal reproductive organs of boys and girls reach maturity and become functional. Although the effect on these organs cannot be seen, the effect on the rest of the body can, in the form of secondary sexual characteristics. The average age for girls to reach puberty is 10-14, though in some cases it begins as early as 8-9. For boys the average age is 13–16.

The effects of hormones in puberty

In girls, the ovaries are stimulated by two hormones: follicle-stimulating hormone (FSH) and luteinising hormone (LH). These

are known as gonadotrophins and they are secreted by the anterior lobe of the pituitary. They have the following effects:

- uterus, fallopian tubes and ovaries reach maturity and become functional
- ovulation and the menstrual cycle begin
- growth of pubic and axillary hair
- glandular tissue in the breasts enlarges and develops
- increase in height and pelvic width
- increase in amount of subcutaneous fat.

In boys, the same gonadotrophins are produced (follicle-stimulating hormone (FSH) and luteinising

hormone (LH), though luteinising hormone is called interstitial cell-stimulating hormone (ICSH) in men and it stimulates the testes to produce testosterone. Most of the changes produced are caused by testosterone and the effects are:

- growth of muscle and bone
- noticeable height increase
- voice breaks and larynx enlarges
- growth of pubic, facial, axillary, abdominal and chest hair
- sexual organs develop
- seminiferous tubules (in the testes; produce testosterone and sperm) become functional and semen can be produced
- sperm production begins.

THE ENDOCRINE SYSTEM

THE MENSTRUAL CYCLE

One of the most important functions of hormones is to prepare the body for reproduction. In a male this involves sperm production. In a female, it involves producing ova (eggs) and preparing the womb so that a fertilised egg can grow into a baby. Whether an egg is fertilised or not, the process of preparing a woman's body for having a baby happens every month. This is known as the menstrual cycle. The start of menstruation (for the first time) is called the menarche. Every 28 days from puberty to menopause (approximately 35 years) the body will prepare itself for a baby and if fertilisation does not take place the body will undo its preparations before starting again a few weeks later. There are three stages:

● *first (menstrual) phase*
● *second (proliferative) phase*
● *third (secretory) phase.*

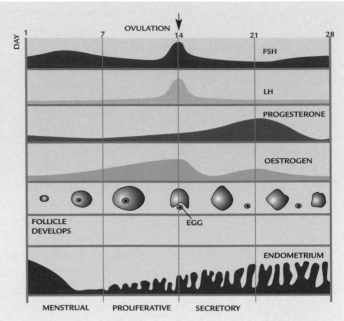

First (menstrual) phase

This lasts for approximately five days. Progesterone produced by the corpus luteum enters the bloodstream and the pituitary gland responds by producing less luteinising hormone. But less luteinising hormone means the corpus luteum begins to break down, the progesterone level falls which stops the endometrium from holding fluid and it starts to break down as well. Menstruation begins as a result of the breakdown of the endometrium. Menstrual flow contains:

● the extra mucus secretions
● the cells lining the uterus
● blood from broken capillaries in endometrium
● the unfertilised ovum.

DAY 1–7

MENSTRUAL

Second (proliferative) phase

This lasts for approximately 7 days. Follicle-stimulating hormone (FSH) is produced in the anterior lobe of the pituitary gland and this stimulates the follicles of the ovaries to produce oestrogen. These follicles are small structures on the surface of the ovary. The oestrogen then stimulates the endometrium (the lining of the womb), promoting the growth of new blood vessels and mucus-producing cells (hence the name proliferative, meaning reproduction and growth). At the end of this stage ovulation occurs: a mature Graafian follicle ruptures releasing a single egg which then travels along the Fallopian tube to the uterus.

DAY 7–14

PROLIFERATIVE

DAY 14–28

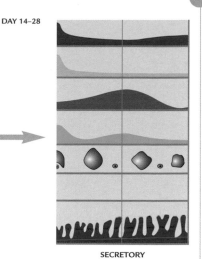

SECRETORY

Third (secretory) phase

This lasts for approximately 14 days. Luteinising hormone (LH), secreted in the anterior lobe of the pituitary gland, stimulates the ruptured follicle lining to grow into corpus luteum – a temporary structure formed by the effect of this hormone on the ruptured ovarian follicle. The corpus luteum produces progesterone thus stimulating the endometrium to retain fluid and produce mucus, which makes it easier for sperm to pass through the reproductive tract. After ovulation, the egg can only be fertilised during the next 8-24 hours. If it is not fertilised, the menstrual phase begins.

As soon as progesterone levels drop (a result of the collapse of the corpus luteum and endometrium), the pituitary gland starts the production of FSH again, and thus stimulates the ovaries to produce another follicle and then another ovum. The cycle begins again.

When does the menstrual cycle stop happening?

Once the menarche (start of menstruation) has passed menstruation only stops in three instances: the onset of amenorrhea (see Diseases and Disorders for more information), pregnancy or the menopause.

Menopause (climacteric)

A woman can, technically speaking, bear children as long as she is menstruating. This reproductive period lasts about 35 years, until the ova (egg) supply is exhausted. Women are born with a certain number of eggs. When these run out, the menopause begins. The average age for menopause to begin is 45-55 and it takes an average of five years to complete (though it can last ten). During this period the hormonal changes that began with puberty will be reversed. For example the ovaries will gradually stop responding to FSH and LH, the hormones that provoked changes in puberty, and thus produce less oestrogen and progesterone. The reduction in these hormones causes irregular menstrual cycles (before menstruation stops completely), shrunken breasts, less hair growth on the body, flushes, sweats, palpitations, atrophied sex organs and possibly unpredictable behaviour. Many of these symptoms of the menopause can be alleviated by use of Hormone Replacement Therapy (HRT).

You now know the endocrine system's structure and function. The final section explains some of the diseases which affect it.

DISEASES AND DISORDERS

Addison's syndrome

Cause: hyposecretion of adrenocortical hormones (sex, growth and salt regulation hormones).
Effects: muscular atrophy and weakness; hypotension; gastric problems like vomiting, changes in skin pigmentation, irregular menstrual cycle and dehydration.

Amenorrhoea

Cause: can be caused by hypersecretion

of testosterone (in females), stress; radical weight loss, anaemia.
Effect: absence of menstruation.

Cushing's syndrome
Cause: hypersecretion of adrenocortical hormones (sex, growth and salt regulation hormones) i.e. the opposite of Addison's syndrome.
Effects: muscular atrophy and weakness, hypertension, moon-shaped face, redistribution of body fat, sometimes mental illness, osteoporosis.

Pre-menstrual syndrome
Cause: onset of menstruation; usually occurs about one week before.
Effects: depression, irritability, bloating, swollen and tender breast tissue, restlessness.

Polycystic ovarian syndrome
(also known as Stein-Leventhal syndrome)
Cause: not known.
Effects: irregular menstrual cycle, due to excessive stimulation of the ovaries by secretion of luteinising hormone, multiple growth of follicular ovarian cysts and sometimes infertility, enlarged ovaries and often high levels of oestrogen; 50% of patients are obese and become hirsute; age range of sufferers is usually 16-30.

Stress
Stress is a threat to the body and the body responds to it like any other danger – the adrenal medulla releases adrenaline and noradrenaline to help us with the fight or flight response. The physical manifestations of the arrival of adrenaline in the body are faster heart rate and breathing, sweating (hence sweaty palms when we are frightened or nervous), a glucose rush from the liver and heightened senses (like hearing and sight). Prolonged stress may cause amenorrhoea in women and low production of sperm in men.

Interrelationships
Endocrine system links to:
Nervous: works very closely with the nervous system to provide homeostasis – balance in the body. The pituitary gland (endocrine) has an infinite link to the hypothalamus (nervous system/brain) both of which exert great control over the body.
Circulatory: hormones are secreted and carried in the bloodstream to the various target organs.
Digestive: digestion is reliant upon hormones secreted in the stomach, small intestines and pancreas.
Reproductive: governs the reproductive system particularly in females as it controls the menstrual cycle and the release of hormones during pregnancy and childbirth.

● SUMMARY

The endocrine system:
- *consists of ductless glands*
- *produces hormones which affect behaviour and function*
- *plays a major role in growth, puberty, the reproductive cycle (menstruation, production of sperm, pregnancy, menopause), responses to stress, kidney and digestive functions.*

The Reproductive System

The reproductive system enables humans to reproduce.

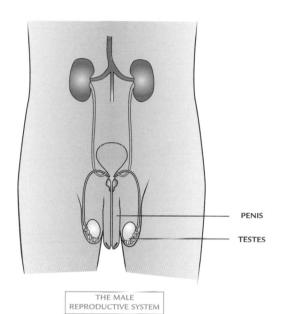

PENIS

TESTES

THE MALE
REPRODUCTIVE SYSTEM

In Brief

Unlike many of the other anatomical systems in the body, the organs in this system differ completely in men and women. In men, they include the prostate gland, testes, testicular vessels, penis and scrotum and in women they include the ovaries, Fallopian tubes, uterus, cervix, vagina and labia. In both sexes, the pelvic girdle is the bony cavity which protects the organs.

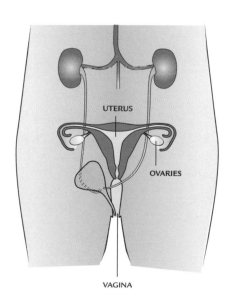

UTERUS

OVARIES

VAGINA

THE FEMALE
REPRODUCTIVE SYSTEM

Learning objectives

The target knowledge of this chapter is:
- the structure and function of the male reproductive system
- the structure and function of the female reproductive system
- the different stages of the reproductive cycle: menstruation and pregnancy
- diseases and disorders of the reproductive system.

THE REPRODUCTIVE SYSTEM

MALE REPRODUCTIVE SYSTEM

The male reproductive system is more visible than the female system, with most of the organs outside the body. This, as you will discover, is for a very good reason.

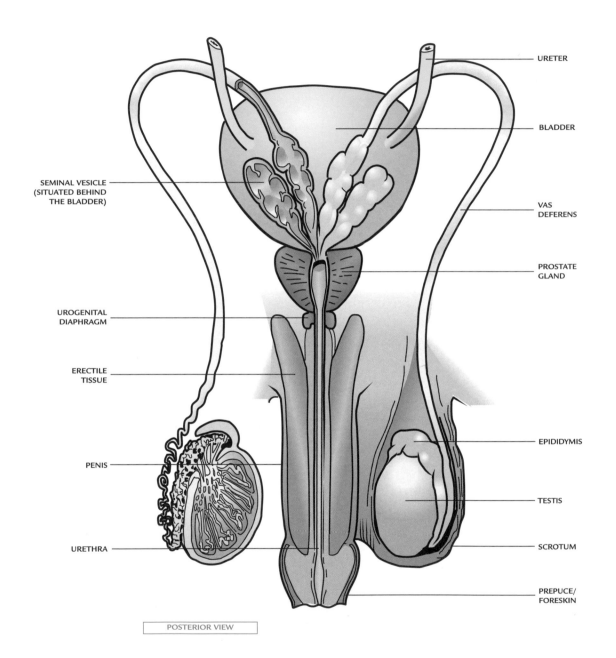

URETER

BLADDER

SEMINAL VESICLE
(SITUATED BEHIND
THE BLADDER)

VAS
DEFERENS

PROSTATE
GLAND

UROGENITAL
DIAPHRAGM

ERECTILE
TISSUE

EPIDIDYMIS

PENIS

TESTIS

URETHRA

SCROTUM

PREPUCE/
FORESKIN

POSTERIOR VIEW

What is the pelvic girdle?
The pelvic girdle is the bony cavity which forms a protective basin for the reproductive organs. Both men and women have one, although it is wider in women to allow for the passage of a baby in childbirth.

Structure: the pelvis is a circle of bones, consisting of the two hip, or innominate bones (each one combining three bones fused together: ilium, ischium and pubis) and, anteriorly, the symphysis pubis, the cartilaginous link between the left and right sides of the girdle. Posteriorly, the sacrum forms the back of the girdle.

Functions: the pelvic girdle protects the internal organs of the reproductive system, as well as the bladder and rectum. It supports the spine and provides attachments for the muscles of the lower back, abdomen and thighs.

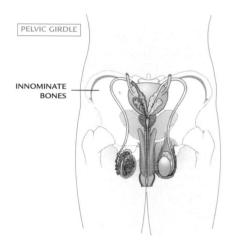

PELVIC GIRDLE

INNOMINATE BONES

What is the prostate gland?

Structure: the prostate is a small gland situated between the bladder and the rectum. It surrounds the beginning of the urethra (known as the prostatic urethra).

Functions: the prostate's position, at the start of the urethra, is important because it produces two secretions carried in semen. One secretion helps keep the lining of the urethra moist and the other is

part of the seminal fluids, which help semen to travel along the urethra and into the female.

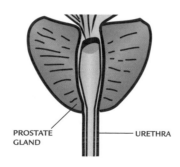

PROSTATE GLAND — URETHRA

What are the testes?

The testes (testis or testicle singular) are the male gonads or glands.

Structure: testes are two glands contained within a sac of skin and muscle called the scrotum. They develop in the abdomen before descending into the scrotum just before birth.

Functions: the testes produce spermatozoa (also known as sperm) and the male sex hormone testosterone which is responsible for male sexual characteristics. Spermatozoa develop in the testes, and are also stored there because they must be kept at a slightly lower temperature than the average body temperature (35°C).

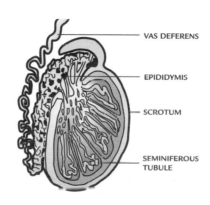

VAS DEFERENS

EPIDIDYMIS

SCROTUM

SEMINIFEROUS TUBULE

What are the testicular vessels?

The testicular vessels are the epididymis and the vas deferens, two tubes which form the passageway from the testes to the urethra.

Epididymis

Structure: the epididymis is a tightly coiled tube. It opens from the top of each testis, continues down along the side of the gland then straightens out into the vas deferens.

Functions: to store and transport sperm as well as acting as a site where immature sperm can develop.

Vas deferens

Structure: a duct with muscular walls leading from the epididymis to the urethra.

Function: the vas deferens acts as a passageway for the transfer of sperm from the storage site of the epididymis to the prostatic urethra and eventually to the penis. This occurs during sexual activity. By contracting its muscular walls the vas deferens pushes the sperm forward.

Scrotum

One of two external sex organs in the male, the scrotum is a sac which contains the testes, epididymis and vas deferens. It hangs under the penis.

Structure: a sac made of an outer layer of skin and an inner layer of muscle. A membrane divides it into two halves, one for each testis.

THE REPRODUCTIVE SYSTEM

Functions: to support and protect the testes as well as maintain the correct temperature for them. The testes are kept outside the body in order to keep them at a slightly lower temperature than the body. However, if the temperature in the scrotum drops, it reacts by contracting its muscular walls, thus moving itself and the testes closer to the body and thus raising the temperature of the glands. If the temperature is too high, the muscles relax, moving the scrotum and testes away from the body and thus lowering the temperature.

Penis

The penis is the main external sex organ of the male. It has three important parts: erectile tissue bodies, the foreskin and the urethra.

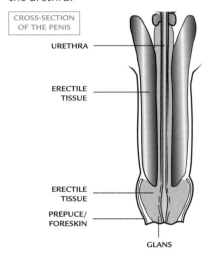

CROSS-SECTION OF THE PENIS

URETHRA

ERECTILE TISSUE

ERECTILE TISSUE

PREPUCE/ FORESKIN

GLANS

Structure: the penis consists of three bodies of spongy, erectile tissue all running lengthways. Two of these run side by side above the urethra, a tube that runs through the centre of the penis and acts as a duct for urine and semen. The third lies underneath them, forming a tube containing the urethra which becomes the tip of the penis, known as the 'glans'. This tissue is full of blood vessels. Surrounding the glans is the prepuce, or foreskin, a loose double fold of skin which protects the glans. The foreskin is sometimes removed either to prevent infection or for religious reasons.

Functions: the penis has a double role –
● organ of excretion. It carries urine from the bladder for excretion.
● organ of reproduction. During sexual activity the penis becomes erect. This 'erection' is caused by an increase in the amount of blood circulating in the vessels of the spongy tissues. These tissues then swell up causing the penis to enlarge. Eventually, the tissues become rigid which allows penetration into the vagina of the female and safe delivery of the semen during intercourse.

What is a sperm?

Structure: sperm look like microscopic tadpoles. Each one consists of a head (the male sex cell), a middle section and a tail, which helps to propel the sperm along the vagina and into the uterus. The head is a nucleus that contains 23 chromosomes whereas the tail is a flagellum, a projection resembling a thread, which moves backwards and forwards enabling the sperm to 'swim' to its destination.

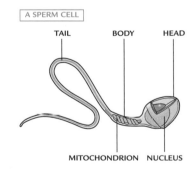

A SPERM CELL

TAIL   BODY   HEAD

MITOCHONDRION   NUCLEUS

Function: sperm fertilise the ova (singular: ovum) that the female reproductive system produces. Ova, or eggs, are the female sex cells. The head of the sperm, carrying the important genetic information in the form of chromosomes, inserts itself into the ovum and the tail, which is no longer needed, breaks down. Although semen (the fluid ejaculated during intercourse) contains millions of sperm, only one is needed to fertilise an ovum. Once fertilised, the ovum usually grows and develops into a baby.

What is semen?
Semen is the fluid discharged from the penis during sexual intercourse. It contains sperm and secretions from the prostate gland and seminal vesicle (a small structure behind the bladder).

Did you know?
When sexual activity takes place, the body's reflexes stop urine from entering the urethra.

You now know all the names and functions of the different organs in the male reproductive system. The next section explains the female reproductive system.

FEMALE REPRODUCTIVE SYSTEM

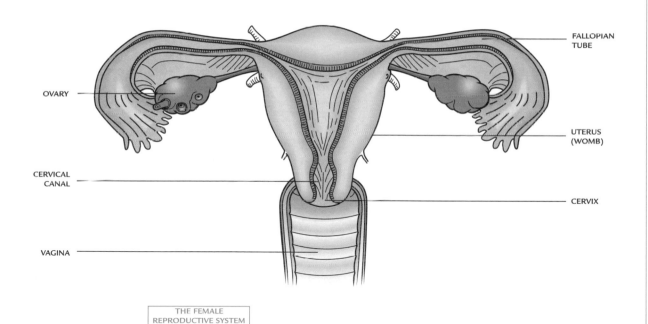

OVARY

CERVICAL CANAL

VAGINA

FALLOPIAN TUBE

UTERUS (WOMB)

CERVIX

THE FEMALE REPRODUCTIVE SYSTEM

This system is hidden inside the body, apart from the entrance to the vagina and the vulva. Just like the male system, the organs within the body are contained and protected by the pelvic girdle. This bony cavity has the same structure in men and women but is wider in the female, in order to allow room for the passage of a baby.

What is the uterus?
The centre of the female reproductive system is the uterus, also known as the womb. It is here that a fertilised ovum grows into a baby. The top end opens out into the Fallopian tubes (which lead to the ovaries) and the bottom end, or cervix, opens into the vagina and forms the birth canal.

Structure: the uterus is a muscular, hollow organ that sits at a right angle to the vagina and connects with the Fallopian tubes. It is the size and shape of an upside-down pear, about 7.5cm long and 5cm wide and expands during pregnancy to accommodate the foetus. The lining of the uterus consists of layers of tissues which respond to hormonal secretions. These layers thicken every month ready to act as a nourishing bed for the fertilised ovum.

Function: the uterus is the place where the foetus grows and develops. Every month it prepares itself for a possible pregnancy and if there is no fertilised ovum, menstruation occurs (*see Menstrual Cycle on page 90*).

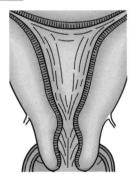

THE UTERUS

What is the cervix?
Structure: the cervix is the narrow neck of the uterus which opens into the vagina. Usually it is the width of a pencil lead but during childbirth it dilates to allow the passage of the baby.

Function: the cervix forms the first part of the birth canal. The dilation of the cervix is a measurement used to determine how soon childbirth will begin.

What are the ovaries?
The ovaries are the female gonads or glands.

Structure: the ovaries are glands. They are approximately the size and shape of almonds and they are positioned either side of the uterus, just below the Fallopian tubes.

Function: the ovaries secrete the hormones responsible for female sexual characteristics (progesterone and oestrogen) as well as storing female sex cells called ova or eggs (singular: ovum). Unlike sperm, ova exist in the body at birth, but in an immature and undeveloped form in follicles. After puberty one of these follicles will develop and rupture, releasing an ovum every month. This is known as ovulation (*see Menstrual Cycle*).

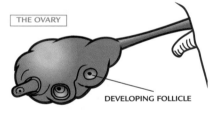

THE OVARY

DEVELOPING FOLLICLE

What is a follicle?
These are small structures on the surface of the ovary, which are known as Graafian follicles when they mature. They contain fluid and an egg or ovum. As soon as an ovum is mature and ready to be fertilised, the follicle splits, releasing the ovum which then travels along the Fallopian tube to the uterus.

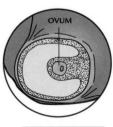

OVUM

MATURE FOLLICLE

What are the Fallopian tubes?
Structure: the Fallopian tubes are funnel-shaped tubes which start at the top of the uterus and continue along to the ovaries. They are named after the Italian anatomist who discovered them.

Functions: the Fallopian tubes are a passageway from the ovaries to the uterus for the ovum, as well as the site of fertilisation. Sperm swim up these tubes to reach the ovum.

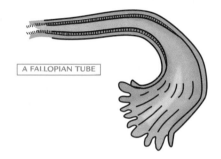

A FALLOPIAN TUBE

What is the vagina?
Structure: the vagina is a muscular passage leading from the cervix to the vulva. It connects the internal sex organs with those on the outside of the body. During sexual activity the blood vessels in the vaginal walls fill with blood causing them to swell and become engorged.

Functions: the vagina connects the cervix to the vulva, and thus to the outside of the body. It serves as a passageway for menstrual blood, forms part of the birth canal during labour and is the site of penetration during intercourse. The external organs of the female reproductive system are known collectively as the vulva. They include the mons pubis, the labia majora and minora and the clitoris.

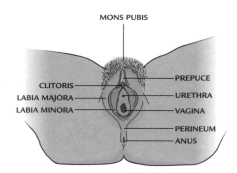

Structure: the breasts are glands which sit on the front of the female chest (men also have breasts, but they are undeveloped). Their size varies considerably. Each breast is circular and convex, with a central, raised nipple. Breasts consist of adipose and areolar tissue supported by fascia. The tissue forms lobes, subdivided into lobules, which open into several ducts. These ducts open on the surface of the

Mons pubis: a protective pad of fat over the symphysis pubis which is covered in hair after puberty.

Labia majora: two large folds of fatty tissue which run lengthways either side of the vulva from the mons pubis to the perineum (skin and tissues between the sex organs and the anus). They protect the entrance to the vagina and urethra.

Labia minora: two smaller folds of skin within the labia majora which surround the clitoris and form a hood (prepuce) to protect it.

Clitoris: a very small, sensitive organ which contains erectile tissue like the penis. It is situated just below the mons pubis. During sexual activity the erectile tissues fill with blood and swell.

The breasts

The breasts are accessory organs to the reproductive system. Although not directly involved in the process of reproduction, they develop during pregnancy ready for their function as milk-secreting glands.

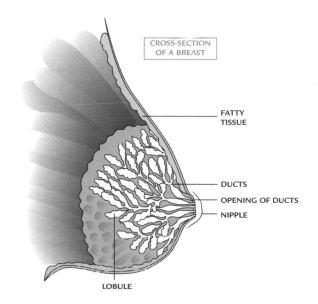

nipple. During pregnancy the lobules develop and produce milk. Hormones cause the breasts to grow during puberty and then activate the secretion of milk during pregnancy.

Function: to secrete milk post-pregnancy.

You now know the structure and function of both male and female reproductive systems. The next section explains how reproduction works.

Did you know?

The female body is capable of producing 35 children in an average lifetime!

PREGNANCY

There are six main stages of pregnancy.

Fertilisation

Post-ovulation, the ovum enters the Fallopian tube in the direction of the

uterus. It reaches the centre of the tube in around 30 minutes. If sperm (in semen) have been deposited in the vagina within 24 hours of ovulation, there is a three day window in which fertilisation may occur. Several hundred sperm (out of the many million deposited) will have swum through the uterus and into the Fallopian tubes in the search for an ovum. Only one sperm is needed to fertilise an ovum. The sperm penetrates the ovum's membrane and enters the ovum. This is fertilisation.

Post-fertilisation
The tail of the sperm breaks down and its head or nucleus grows. The nucleus of the sperm and the nucleus of the ovum fuse to make a single nucleus. Within this new nucleus, the male and female chromosomes join up forming the zygote, the first cell of a new baby.

Cell division
Once the zygote has formed, it

undergoes a process of mitotic cell division, dividing into two, then four, then eight cells and so on until a ball of cells, called a morula, is formed. After five days this develops into a blastocyst (a multi-celled structure) which enters the uterus and implants in the endometrium of the uterus on the seventh day (post-fertilisation).

Formation of embryo
By day 24 the blastocyst has formed an amniotic cavity (a fluid-filled sac) containing an embryo that looks a little like a seahorse. The endometrium and part of the blastocyst mesh and develop into the placenta, the baby's support system (which allows the passage of nutrients, oxygen and waste to and from baby and mother).

Development of foetus
The embryo is known as the foetus from eight weeks. It develops in the amniotic cavity. The fluid protects the baby from shocks and pressure and allows it to grow unhindered.

Birth (parturition)
Just before birth, the membrane of the amniotic cavity breaks and the amniotic fluid is released via the vagina. Childbirth usually occurs in the 40th week after fertilisation.

You now know the names and functions of the male and female reproductive systems, how menstruation and reproduction occur. The final section explains some of the diseases and disorders of the reproductive system.

DISEASES AND DISORDERS

Ectopic pregnancy
This is a pregnancy which occurs outside the uterus. A fertilised ovum may develop inside the Fallopian tube instead of travelling to the uterus. There is a danger of haemorrhage and death.

Amenorrhoea
Causes: can be caused by hypersecretion of testosterone in females, other hormonal imbalances, stress, radical weight loss, anaemia or excessive exercise.
Effect: absence of menstruation.

Dysmenorrhoea
Causes: spasm or congestion of

the uterus, imbalance in hormones or emotional disturbances.
Effect: extremely difficult and painful menstruation.

Pre-menstrual syndrome
Cause: onset of menstruation; usually occurs about one week before.
Effect: depression, irritability, bloating and water retention, swollen and tender breast tissue (mastalgia), restlessness.

Polycystic ovarian syndrome
(also known as Stein-Leventhal syndrome)
Cause: hyposecretion of female sex

hormones (luteinising hormone).
Effect: irregular menstrual cycle, multiple growth of follicular ovarian cysts and sometimes infertility, enlarged ovaries, 50% of patients are obese and become hirsute (hairy); age range of sufferers is usually 16-30.

Cancers
Cancer is the development of malignant cells. It can occur in breasts, ovaries, the cervix, testes and/or prostate gland.

Interrelationships
Reproductive links to:
Endocrine: hormones from the endocrine system govern the reproductive system particularly in females.
Nervous: sexual stimulus is relayed by nerve impulses.

SUMMARY
The reproductive system
● *is different and complementary in men and women*
● *is dedicated to the reproduction of the species.*

The Digestive System

The alimentary canal is composed of the mouth, oesophagus, stomach, small and large intestine.

In Brief

Without food, water and oxygen, human beings could not survive. The digestive system is the set of organs which transform whatever we eat into substances that can be used in the body for energy, growth and repair. Once the food has been broken down by various chemical processes, and the nutrients removed, the rest is excreted as waste. The whole process involves many different organs and sometimes takes several hours.

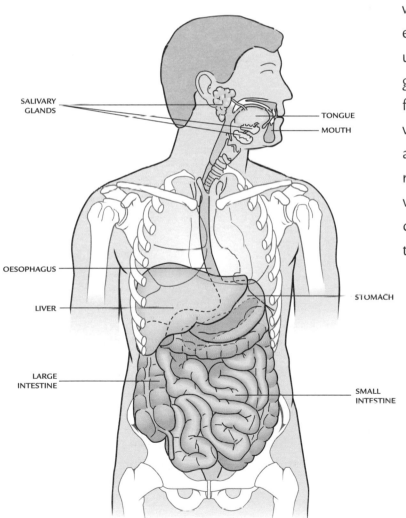

SALIVARY GLANDS

TONGUE

MOUTH

OESOPHAGUS

STOMACH

LIVER

LARGE INTESTINE

SMALL INTESTINE

THE DIGESTIVE SYSTEM

Learning objectives ●

The target knowledge of this chapter is:
- the structure of the digestive system
- the function of the digestive system
- the four stages of digestion
- the chemistry of digestion
- the function of enzymes
- diseases and disorders of the digestive system.

DIGESTION

What is digestion?

The breakdown and transformation of solid and liquid food into microscopic substances. These substances are then transported by the blood into different areas of the body. There are four stages of digestion:

Mouth: ingestion (the taking in of food or liquid into the body), chewing and swallowing; start of starch digestion
Stomach: mixing and protein digestion
Small intestine: carbohydrate and fat digestion; absorption
Large intestine: waste and excretion.

Section 1: the mouth

Where does digestion start?

In the mouth where the action of teeth and saliva combine in the first stage of breakdown, chewing and partially digesting the food so that it will pass more easily along the oesophagus. The ball of food that leaves the mouth is known as a bolus.

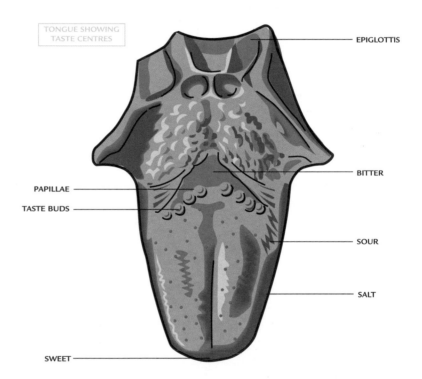

TONGUE SHOWING TASTE CENTRES

EPIGLOTTIS

PAPILLAE

TASTE BUDS

BITTER

SOUR

SALT

SWEET

What is saliva?

Saliva is a liquid secreted by three pairs of salivary glands: the parotid gland (situated below the ear), the submandibular gland and the sublingual gland (both situated below the tongue). It contains water, mucus and the enzyme salivary amylase.

Saliva has three functions:

- to lubricate the food with mucus, making it easier to swallow
- to start digestion: it contains the enzyme salivary amylase, which acts on cooked starch turning it into shorter polysaccharides
- to keep the mouth and teeth clean.

What is an enzyme?

If you think about the food you eat, and the difference in size between it and the microscopic cells and tissues that it will feed and support in your body, it is easy to understand why a digestive system that breaks food down into different units is needed. Enzymes are an important part of the process. If the digestive system is a conveyor belt, enzymes are the machines and workers which slowly change whatever is on the belt to make it smaller and smaller so that, eventually, it can be carried around the body in blood. They are made of protein and act as catalysts i.e. they make chemical changes happen in other substances, whilst themselves remaining unchanged. They act on food, changing it into smaller particles.

What is the tongue?

Structure: the tongue is a muscular organ, covered with a membrane. It is held in place by attachments to the mandible (lower jaw) and the hyoid bone. Tiny projections known as papillae cover the top, increasing its surface area and producing a rough texture. At the sides and base of the tongue, as well as on the palate and at the back of the throat, there are special areas known as taste buds.

Functions: the tongue has three digestive functions — taste, chewing and swallowing:
- **taste**: the tongue is covered with thousands of taste buds which are sensitive to salt, sweet, sour and bitter chemicals in food and drink. They help us enjoy what we eat and drink and act as the first line of defence, warning us when food, drink or foreign matter are off or inedible.
- **chewing**: the tongue aids chewing by moving food around the mouth, pushing it between the teeth and covering it with saliva, which contains

What is a polysaccharide?

There are three types of saccharides: monosaccharides, disaccharides and polysaccharides. They are all forms of carbohydrates — the sugars and starches used by the body for energy. Enzymes at various stages in the digestive process break down starches and sugars like those in bread, cakes, biscuits and potatoes into different sorts of saccharides. A monosaccharide is a simple sugar (mono- means one) whereas disaccharides and polysaccharides are complex sugars.

enzymes that start the digestive process. The food is turned into a partially digested mass known as a bolus.
- **swallowing**: when the food is ready to travel to the stomach, the tongue pushes it to the back of the mouth.

How does food get from the mouth to the stomach?

Via the action of swallowing and through the tube known as the oesophagus. The tongue pushes the bolus to the back of the mouth, towards the pharynx, a muscular tube behind the mouth. The food passes into the pharynx and down to the oesophagus. The epiglottis, a small flap of cartilage which forms part of the larynx (the windpipe) moves upwards and forwards, blocking the entrance to the larynx. This stops the food from 'going down the wrong way' and prevents choking.

What is the oesophagus?

Structure: the oesophagus is a muscular tube which leads from the pharynx, at the back of the mouth, to the stomach, the first main organ of digestion.

Function: to carry chewed food from the pharynx to the stomach. Food moves along it by a muscular contraction known as peristalsis. The muscle fibres contract and relax which acts like a wave on the tube, pushing the bolus forwards. The lining of the oesophagus secretes mucus to ease and lubricate the passage of food.

Section 2: the stomach

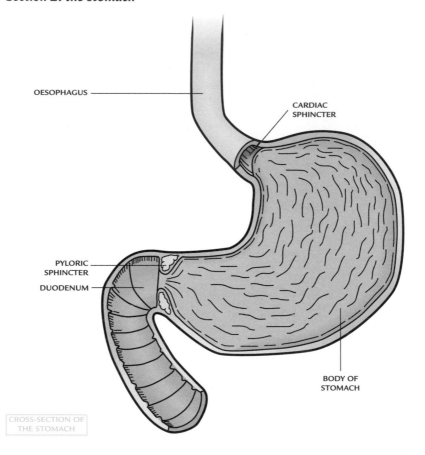

OESOPHAGUS

CARDIAC SPHINCTER

PYLORIC SPHINCTER

DUODENUM

BODY OF STOMACH

CROSS-SECTION OF THE STOMACH

What is the stomach?

Structure: the stomach is a J-shaped, elastic organ which expands and contracts depending on what is in it. Food enters it from the oesophagus via the cardiac sphincter, a valve that stops back flow of the stomach's contents, and leaves it through the pyloric sphincter into the duodenum, the first part of the small intestine. The wall of the stomach is a combination of layers of muscle fibre with an inner mucous membrane. The latter has lots of folds, called rugae. When the stomach is full they stretch out, enabling expansion, then they contract when it empties.

What does it do?

Functions:

● digests proteins through the action of enzymes

● churns food with gastric juices
● helps to lubricate the food by producing mucus (from the mucous membrane)
● absorbs alcohol
● kills bacteria by producing hydrochloric acid.

Gastric juices contain:

● **hydrochloric acid**: neutralises bacteria and activates pepsin
● **rennin**: enzyme that curdles milk protein (only in infants)
● **pepsin**: enzyme that acts on proteins turning them into peptones.

At this stage proteins have been partially digested and, along with the carbohydrates such as starch which were partially digested in the mouth, they have to wait until the small intestine to complete digestion.

The chemistry of digestion

The whole digestive process is a combination of different chemical reactions that act on the food we eat, reducing it to the building blocks of nutrients for absorption and use by the body. Every piece of food we eat is composed of fats, carbohydrates (or starches) and proteins. These must be broken down into their relative chemical compounds in order for the body to use them i.e. by the time the bread you eat reaches your muscles as energy it has been chewed, churned, liquefied and the starch changed to useable glucose. The following shows the main chemical reactions and breakdowns at different stages of digestion.

What are proteins?

Proteins are made up of one or more interlinked polypeptide chains and are the building material for the body. Protein foods include dairy products, meat, fish and beans. In order to be used by the body they must be converted into a chemical compound called an amino acid. There are approximately 20 amino acids and two types: essential and non-essential. Essential amino acids are those which the body cannot make itself and must be supplied by diet and non-essential amino acids are those which the body can make enough of and are not therefore a dietary requirement. They are broken down as follows:

- proteins are first broken down by pepsin, an enzyme in the stomach, into peptones, which are partially digested proteins.
- peptones are then broken down by enzymes in the small intestine (trypsin, chymotrypsin) into polypeptides, structures formed from groups of amino acids.
- finally, the enzyme peptidase, in the small intestine, breaks the polypeptides into individual amino acids, ready for absorption.

What are fats?

Fats are the body's purest energy source. In order to be absorbed by the body, they need to be converted to fatty acids and glycerol which are compounds that can be absorbed by the small intestine. This process takes place as follows:

- fats are emulsified by bile salts (which come from the liver to the duodenum).
- emulsified fats are broken down in the duodenum by the enzyme lipase, found in pancreatic juice, and converted to fatty acids and glycerol.
- fatty acids and glycerol are absorbed in the small intestine.

What is an emulsified fat?

To emulsify means to turn into an emulsion, a liquid that carries another liquid within it in suspension. An emulsified fat is one that has been turned into a liquid and carried by bile. Some paints are known as emulsions because they are precisely that. Many medicines, including milk of magnesia, are emulsions.

What are carbohydrates?

Carbohydrates (sugars and starches, found in bread, pasta, biscuits and cakes) are the energy providers for the body. They are partially digested in the mouth but are not fully digested until they reach the small intestine. They are broken down as follows:

- in the mouth the enzyme salivary amylase acts on cooked starches (which are polysaccharides) and converts them to shorter polysaccharides (complex sugars).
- the enzyme amylase converts the polysaccharides to disaccharides in the duodenum.
- the action of the enzymes maltase, lactase and sucrase in the small intestine converts disaccharides into monosaccharides which are then absorbed.

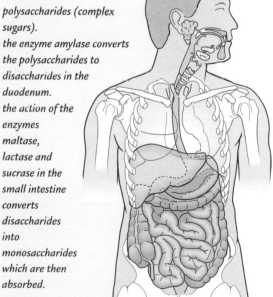

Section 3: the small intestine

What is the small intestine?

The small intestine, ironically, is not that small. It is seven metres long and divided into three different parts: the duodenum, the jejunum and the ileum. The walls have four layers, including a muscular layer, a layer containing blood vessels, lymph vessels and nerves and an inner mucous membrane. The inner wall is covered with villi, tiny finger-like projections which increase the surface area for absorption and contain a network of blood and lymph vessels.

What does the small intestine do?

Completion of the chemical digestion of food and the subsequent absorption of nutrients takes place in the small intestine.

Nutrients are absorbed through the villi into the blood and lymph vessels. Hardly any food is absorbed elsewhere in the digestive system.

How does digestion and absorption take place in the small intestine?

1 peristaltic movements mix food with intestinal and pancreatic juices as well as bile. The movements push the food against the villi. Intestinal juices are composed of enzymes:
● maltase, sucrase and lactase which split disaccharides into monosaccharides
● enterokinase which activates trypsin in pancreatic juice
● peptidases which split polypeptides into amino acids e.g trypsin

2 absorption: digested food is absorbed through the walls of the villi:
● fats, fatty acids and glycerol are passed into the lacteals (lymphatic capillaries). They are called lacteals because the fat passes into them in suspension, making the lymph look milky.
● amino acids and sugars pass along the hepatic-portal vein to the liver.

CROSS-SECTION OF WALL OF SMALL INTESTINE

— MUCOUS MEMBRANE
— LACTEAL (LYMPHATIC VESSEL)
— SUBMUCOUS LAYER
— CIRCULAR MUSCLE
— LONGITUDINAL MUSCLE
— PERITONEUM

Organ	Secretion	Action
Mouth Salivary glands	Salivary amylase	Converts starch into shorter chain polysaccharides
Stomach	Rennin Hydrochloric acid Pepsin	Converts milk into curds (in infants) Neutralises bacteria Converts proteins into peptones
Duodenum	1: Pancreatic juice ● trypsin ● lipase ● amylase 2: Bile	 Converts peptones into shorter chain polypeptides Converts fats into fatty acids and glycerol Converts olysaccharides into disaccharides Emulsifies fats
Small intestine (from the villi)	Intestinal juice ● maltase ● sucrase ● lactase ● enterokinase ● peptidases	 Convert disaccharides into monosaccharides Activates trypsin in pancreatic juice Convert polypeptides into amino acids, e.g. trypsin

3 three hormones in the small intestine help digestion: secretin, pancreozymin and enterocrinin. They stimulate the production of pancreatic juices, which in turn stimulate the production of intestinal juices.

Other functions of the small intestine

To protect the digestive system from infection. It is the only section of the digestive system with a direct link to the protective lymphatic system.

Stage 4: the large intestine and waste

What is the large intestine?

The large intestine deals with waste. It is about 1.5m long and sits draped around the small intestine, in an arch shape. It consists of the caecum, appendix, colon, rectum, anal canal and anus.

Functions: to reabsorb water and nutrients from digestive waste and to get rid of waste. Whatever remains of the food, once it has been through the processes of mixing, conversion and absorption carried out in the stomach and small intestine, is passed into the large intestine. Any remaining nutrients are removed and the result is faeces.

Faeces

Faeces are the unwanted leftovers from food, combined with cellulose (roughage which is indigestible, found in foods like vegetables and bran), dead blood cells, bacteria (both living and dead), fatty acids and mucus, used to help move the faeces through the large intestine. The colour comes from the dead blood cells and bilirubin, a bile pigment.

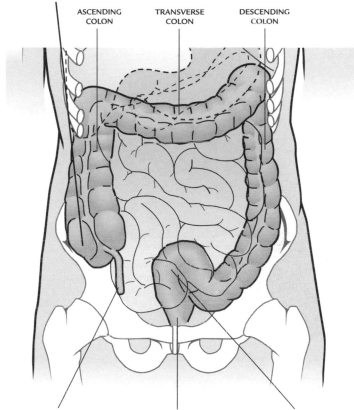

CAECUM: A SMALL POUCH; THE ILEUM EMPTIES ITS CONTENTS INTO THE CAECUM THROUGH THE ILEO-CAECAL VALVE

THE LARGE INTESTINE

ASCENDING COLON

TRANSVERSE COLON

DESCENDING COLON

APPENDIX: NARROW TUBE ATTACHED TO CAECUM; ABOUT 9CM LONG

ANUS: OPENING WITH TWO SPHINCTERS, AN INNER INVOLUNTARY AND AN OUTER VOLUNTARY

RECTUM: ABOUT 12CM LONG; CONTINUOUS WITH THE PELVIC COLON; PASSES FROM COLON THROUGH PELVIC CAVITY TO ANAL CANAL THEN ANUS

Summary of large intestine's functions

- *Absorption of nutrients, vitamins, salt or water left in digestive waste.*
- *Secretion of mucus to help passage of faeces.*
- *Storage of faeces in rectum (short-term because the arrival of faeces in rectum tells brain of need to defecate).*
- *Micro-organism/bacteria activity: many bacteria live in the large intestine. Though they can cause disease they are harmless in the colon and may even be useful.*
- *Defecation: a 'mass movement' pushes waste along the transverse colon, often stimulated by food arriving in the stomach. It is a reflex but humans have control of it. If the reflex is ignored, more water will be absorbed from the faeces which may cause constipation.*

ACCESSORY ORGANS

There are three other organs involved in the digestive process: the liver, pancreas and gall bladder. They are known as accessory organs because, although food doesn't pass directly through them, they help the process, breaking down the toxins/waste that digestion produces.

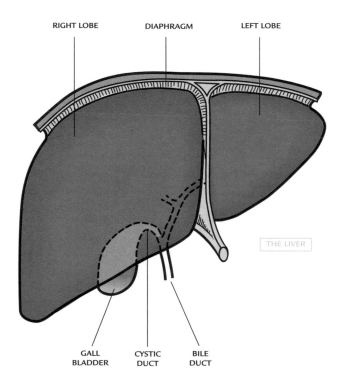

RIGHT LOBE   DIAPHRAGM   LEFT LOBE

THE LIVER

GALL
BLADDER   CYSTIC
DUCT   BILE
DUCT

What is the liver?

Structure: the largest gland in the body, the liver sits at the top of the abdomen, just below the diaphragm and just above and to the right of the medial line. It is vital because it performs many essential functions.

Functions: the liver is vital for cleansing and storage as well as production. It:

removes

- toxins from drugs, alcohol, and harmful substances
- nitrogen from amino acids.

stores

- vitamins A, B12, D, E, K
- glycogen (a compound that stores energy)
- iron, from the breakdown of red blood cells and food
- fats.

produces

- heat (the liver is the body's radiator, producing more heat than any other organ as a result of its various functions)
- vitamin A (from carotene, found in green-leafed vegetables and carrots)
- Vitamin D
- heparin
- plasma proteins: albumin, globulin, prothrombin, fibrinogen
- bile
- uric acid and urea, from breakdown of red blood cells and de-amination of amino acids.

converts

- stored (saturated) fat into other fat products (like cholesterol)
- glycogen to glucose, when energy is needed
- glucose back to glycogen, in presence of insulin
- metabolises protein.

The liver in history

Like parts of the circulation, parts of the digestive system have always been seen as very important throughout history, both for what they do and what they represent. This is especially true with the liver. For example in ancient Rome, animals were sacrificed for their livers before battles. The organs were then used to predict what might happen. For example, a pale liver was bad news and predicted defeat whereas a healthy red liver meant the conditions were favourable for victory. The liquid secreted by the liver, bile, was thought to be one of four body fluids known as humours which determined personality. Black bile (or melancholy) meant a person was sad and choler (or yellow bile) meant they were irritable. A coward's liver was thought to be bloodless, which is why someone cowardly is lily-livered.

What is the gall bladder?

Structure: a pear-shaped sac attached by the cystic and bile ducts to the posterior of the liver. Whenever there is excess bile secreted by the liver which can't be used immediately for digestion, the bile passes first along the bile duct then along the cystic duct to the gall bladder where it will be stored until needed.

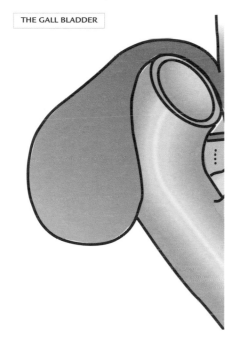

THE GALL BLADDER

Functions:
- reservoir for bile (from liver)
- secretes mucus to add to bile
- absorbs water from bile, making it more concentrated
- contracts in order to empty bile into duodenum.

What is bile?

Structure: a thick liquid produced in the liver as a result of the breakdown of red blood cells. It contains salts, bile pigments, acids and water.

Functions: emulsifying fats, stimulating peristalsis and creating alkaline conditions in the small intestine.

What is insulin?

Insulin is a hormone secreted by specialised cells in the pancreas known as the islets of Langerhans. It regulates blood sugar level. When we eat, the blood sugar level rises. The sugar in the blood is in the form of glucose. Insulin helps cells absorb glucose and turns any excess glucose into glycogen, an insoluble sugar which is stored in the liver until the body needs it. Thus the blood sugar level drops. A lack of insulin causes diabetes mellitus: glucose cannot be properly absorbed into the body resulting in the following symptoms – a dangerously high level of blood sugar, the loss of glucose through excretion, thirstiness and excessive urine production.

What is the pancreas?

Structure: the pancreas is a gland situated behind the stomach, between the duodenum and the spleen. It delivers pancreatic juices to the duodenum through the pancreatic duct. The cells of the pancreas are divided into the islets of Langerhans (which produce insulin) and a network of alveoli (small sac-like cavities). The alveoli are lined with cells that produce enzymes.

Functions: the pancreas works with both the digestive and the endocrine systems, producing enzymes to break down food and the hormone insulin which regulates the blood sugar level after eating. It also produces the hormone glucogen which increases blood glucose levels by converting glycogen back to glucose.
Pancreatic juices contain:
- lipase (fat digestion)
- amylase (starch digestion)
- trypsin (protein digestion).

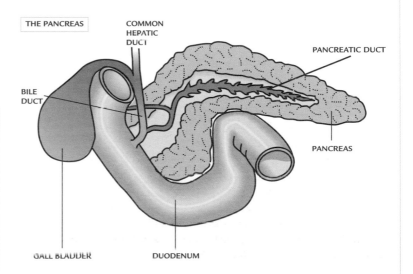

THE PANCREAS — COMMON HEPATIC DUCT — PANCREATIC DUCT — BILE DUCT — PANCREAS — GALL BLADDER — DUODENUM

DISEASES AND DISORDERS

Anorexia

Anorexia is a loss of appetite. Anorexia nervosa is a psychological condition which often affects teenage girls and young women. The sufferers have a fear of gaining weight or being fat and refuse to eat very much or stop eating altogether. It can be severely debilitating and sometimes fatal.

Appendicitis

Acute inflammation of the appendix, usually treated by removal of the organ.

Bulimia

Bulimia is the opposite of anorexia, an insatiable hunger. Bulimia nervosa is a psychological condition which, like anorexia, often affects teenage girls and young women. Symptoms include binge eating followed by evacuation methods such as self-induced vomiting and excessive use of laxatives.

Cirrhosis

Chronic damage to an organ causing hardening. Several types of cirrhosis exist but the most common is cirrhosis of the liver, which is frequently caused by excessive alcohol consumption.

Constipation

Infrequent or uncomfortable bowel movements, causing hard faeces to block the rectum. Caused by lack of fibre in the diet, lack of fluids and lack of exercise. Sometimes caused by stress.

Gall stones

Stones formed from residues of bile pigments, cholesterol and calcium salts, found in the gall bladder.

Heartburn

Burning sensation in oesophagus or throat, caused by back flow and regurgitation of acidic stomach contents.

Hernia

A rupture, in which an organ pushes through the surface of the structures which normally hold it in.

Jaundice

Excessive levels of bile pigments in the blood cause skin to turn yellow. Caused by malfunctioning gall bladder or obstructed flow of bile.

Irritable bowel syndrome

No exact cause is yet known for irritable bowel syndrome (sometimes referred to as IBS), though stress and low-fibre, high fat diets are said to contribute. Symptoms include stomach and bowel pain and alternate bouts of diarrhoea and constipation.

Stress

The most common effect of stress on the digestive system is ulcers.

Anxiety and lack of relaxation cause overproduction of gastric juices and if they have nothing to work on they will start to attack the lining of the stomach or other structures. In short, the stomach starts digesting itself!

Ulcer

Erosion in the walls of the digestive system, often caused by too much acid.

Interrelationships

Digestive system links to:
All systems: provides nutrition to the whole body.
Circulatory: the circulatory system transports nutrients from the digestive system to every system of the body.
Endocrine: the endocrine system secretes certain hormones, which help metabolism.
Lymphatic: lymphatic vessels are found in the lacteals of the villi in the small intestine and help with the absorption of fats.
Muscular: the digestive system supplies glucose for energy to the muscular system: sphincter muscles contract along the alimentary canal to push food along – known as peristalsis.
Nervous: all the organs of the digestive system are stimulated by nerve impulses.

SUMMARY

The digestive system
- *transforms food and drink into nutrients and waste*
- *consists of every process from eating (ingestion) to excretion*
- *relies on chemicals (enzymes) to carry out the break down of food.*

The Respiratory System

The respiratory system consists of the nose, lungs, diaphragm and the air passages, such as the trachea, which connect them.

In Brief

The respiratory system is the body's breathing equipment. Similar to the digestive system, it takes substances from outside the body (gases, particularly oxygen), circulates them through the body to cells and tissues, then excretes the excess and waste. Oxygen is the respiratory system's 'food' and carbon dioxide is its 'waste'. Breathing is the most fundamental action of the human body: we cannot live without it for more than a couple of minutes.

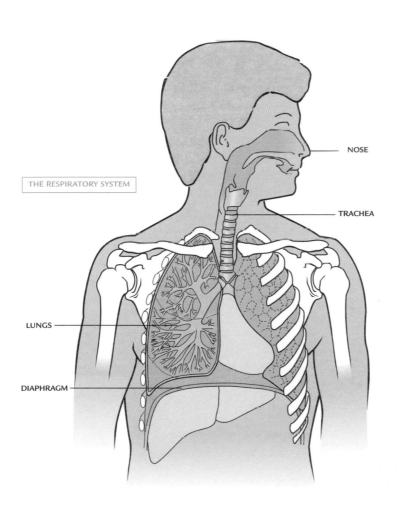

THE RESPIRATORY SYSTEM

NOSE

TRACHEA

LUNGS

DIAPHRAGM

Learning objectives

The target knowledge of this chapter is:
- the structure of the respiratory system
- the function of the respiratory system
- what is external respiration
- what is internal respiration
- how the nervous system controls breathing
- diseases and disorders of the respiratory system.

STRUCTURE

Section 1: how oxygen enters the body: the passage of air from nose to lungs

What is breathing?
Breathing, or external respiration, is the inhalation and exhalation of air and the gases it contains.

How do we breathe?
Through the nose and the system of passageways and organs with which it connects. The nose is the only organ of respiration that we can see. The following section explains the structure and function of the organs of the respiratory system.

What is the nose?
The nose is an organ on the face. It acts as the first passageway for air entering the body.

Structure: the nose is made of cartilage and two nasal bones. It is covered with skin, both inside and out and lined with a mucous membrane that is ciliated i.e. it has microscopic hairs. The two nostrils lead into a bony nasal cavity, which has two chambers, divided by a nasal septum. The septum is made of cartilage. Thus the outside of the nose which we can see, is mostly made of cartilage whereas the inside of the nose is mostly made of bone. The nasal cavity connects to the paranasal sinuses, hollow spaces inside the bones surrounding the nose which are full of air and are also lined with mucous membrane.

Functions: the nose is the first organ that air enters. It has three functions:
- to work as the organ of smell
- to moisten and warm the air entering the nostrils
- to filter dust, bacteria, and other foreign matter from the air using the mucous membrane and its hairs. The mucus collects any dirt and bacteria and prevents it from passing into the lungs. The cilia push the mucus into the throat. It is then swallowed and travels to the stomach where any bacteria are neutralised by gastric acids.

UPPER RESPIRATORY TRACT

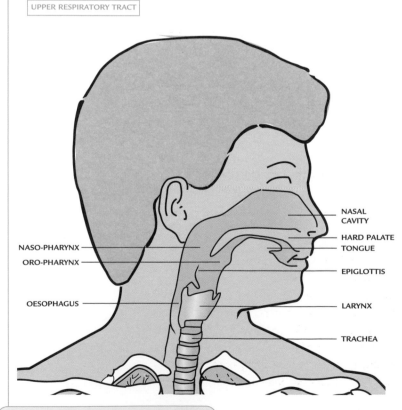

NASAL CAVITY

HARD PALATE

TONGUE

NASO-PHARYNX

ORO-PHARYNX

EPIGLOTTIS

OESOPHAGUS

LARYNX

TRACHEA

Pharynx

Once air has been filtered, moistened and warmed in the nose it travels to the pharynx, a tube which leads from the back of the nose and mouth and divides into the oesophagus (posteriorly) and larynx (anteriorly). It works as part of both the digestive and respiratory systems.

Structure: the pharynx is about 12.5cm long and made of muscular and fibrous tissue. At the back of the section of the pharynx which connects to the nose are small masses of lymphoid tissue which form the pharyngeal tonsils, or adenoids. Like the palatine tonsils (at the junction of the mouth and throat) the pharyngeal tonsils filter bacteria.

Function: it acts as an air passage and also warms and moistens the air.

Larynx

From the pharynx, air travels down to the larynx (also known as the voice box).

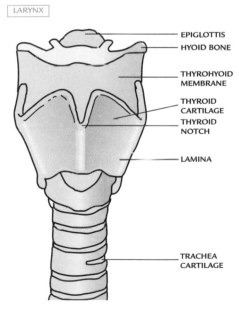

LARYNX

EPIGLOTTIS
HYOID BONE
THYROHYOID MEMBRANE
THYROID CARTILAGE
THYROID NOTCH
LAMINA
TRACHEA CARTILAGE

Structure: the larynx is a tube positioned between the tongue at the back of the mouth and the trachea (the tube leading to the lungs). It is made of rings of cartilage, attached to each other by membranes and ligaments. The thyroid cartilage at the top of the larynx, which is larger in men than in women, forms the Adam's apple which is often visible in the throat.

Function: the larynx is a passageway for air between the pharynx and trachea. It filters bacteria, helps in voice production and warms and moistens the air.

Trachea

From the larynx, air travels to the trachea.

Structure: the trachea is a continuation of the larynx. It is a tube about 10cm long which runs from the front of the neck to the chest where it divides into two bronchi, tubes which lead to the lungs. The trachea is made of incomplete rings of hyaline cartilage (anteriorly) and involuntary muscle and connective tissue (posteriorly). It is lined with ciliated epithelium which contains mucus-secreting goblet cells.

Function: the trachea is a passageway for air between the larynx and bronchi. The goblet secretory cells in the lining secrete mucus which collects any foreign matter or bacteria and the cilia then push this up to the larynx.

Bronchi

The bronchi are the branches of the respiratory tube which transport air in and out of each lung.

Structure: bronchi (singular: bronchus) connect the trachea to the lungs. There are two of them, one on the left and one on the right which enter the lungs at the hilum, a concave depression, where they subdivide into different branches for different lobes of the lungs. Like the trachea, they are made of hyaline cartilage, involuntary muscle and connective tissue and are lined with ciliated epithelium.

Function: to pass air from the trachea into the bronchioles, and thus to the lungs.

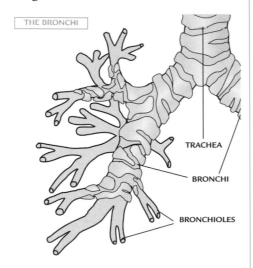

TRACHEA

BRONCHI

BRONCHIOLES

Bronchioles
The final and finest tubes in the passage of air from the nose to the lungs are the bronchioles.

Structure: bronchioles are made of muscular, fibrous and elastic tissue. They become progressively smaller as they spread further into the lungs until they are no more than a single layer of flattened epithelial cells (just like blood capillaries). These microscopic tubes are called terminal bronchioles.

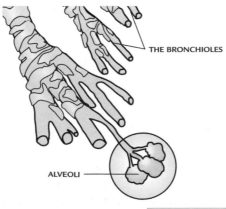

THE BRONCHIOLES

ALVEOLI

Function: bronchioles take air to the alveoli of the lungs.

Lungs
The two lungs are the centre of the respiratory system. It is in these two spongy organs that gases enter and exit the blood.

Structure: the lungs are positioned either side of the heart; the left lung is divided into two lobes, the superior and inferior lobes, whereas the right lung is divided into three, the superior, middle and inferior. Lobes are subdivided into lobules. Lung tissue is made of bronchioles, alveoli, blood vessels, nerves, connective tissue and elastic tissue. They are covered in a special membrane called the pleura.

Function: lungs allow the exchange of gases into and out of the blood.

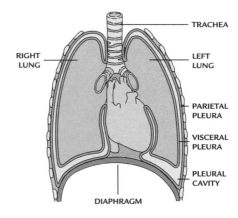

TRACHEA

RIGHT LUNG

LEFT LUNG

PARIETAL PLEURA

VISCERAL PLEURA

PLEURAL CAVITY

DIAPHRAGM

Pleura
Structure: the pleura is a serous membrane that surrounds each lung. It has two layers, the inner, visceral layer which sticks to the lung tissue and covers the surface and the outer, parietal layer which sticks to the chest wall and the top of the diaphragm. The two layers are separated by a space called the pleural cavity which is filled with a serous fluid.

ANATOMY AND PHYSIOLOGY

Function: the pleural cavity prevents friction between the two layers during respiration.

Alveoli

The exchange of gases in the lungs takes place in tiny sacs called alveoli (singular: alveolus) at the end of the terminal bronchioles.

Structure: alveoli are made of a thin layer of squamous epithelial cells and are surrounded by a capillary network.

Function: to exchange gases between the circulatory and respiratory systems. The pulmonary artery delivers deoxygenated blood to the capillary network which is then oxygenated by contact with the air in the alveoli. The oxygenated blood then leaves the lungs via the capillary network and the pulmonary veins and travels to the heart to be pumped around the body.

You now know the names, structures and functions of all the organs and passageways which transmit air from outside the body into the lungs. The next section explains the mechanism of breathing.

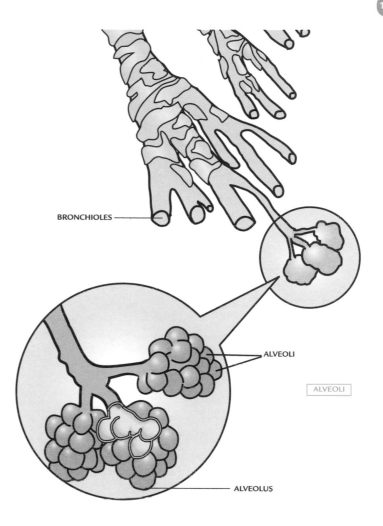

BRONCHIOLES

ALVEOLI

ALVEOLI

ALVEOLUS

Section two: how breathing works — internal and external respiration

Mechanism of respiration

Although all of these separate tubes and passageways have individual functions, it is their function as a whole that is important i.e. to allow us, and every cell in our body, to breathe. The entrance and exit of air in and out of the body is a process known as breathing, whereas the entrance and exit of air in and out of cells is known as gaseous exchange.

What is breathing?

Breathing is the mechanism which enables the entrance and exit of air into

the body as well as the exchange of gases between the blood and the alveoli. In order to understand how the gases pass from one tissue to the next it is important to know the following physical law:

gases diffuse from a higher pressure to a lower pressure until equal pressure is achieved.

Diffusion occurs when a strong concentration of a gas comes into contact with a weak concentration of the same gas. The dissolved gas molecules will move from the strong concentration to the weak concentration until the concentration is equal on both sides. In the case of oxygen and carbon dioxide this occurs through the capillary and alveoli walls. The oxygen in the alveoli is under more pressure than the venous, deoxygenated blood in the capillaries so the oxygen passes from the alveoli (high pressure) into the capillaries (low pressure). Once the pressure in both is the same, the exchange stops. The carbon dioxide in the blood is under more pressure than the carbon dioxide in the alveoli so it diffuses through the capillary walls to the alveoli. The blood is thus oxygenated and its waste removed and it now travels back to the heart ready to be pumped round the body. The lungs then expel the carbon dioxide through the process of exhalation.

What is gaseous exchange?

Once blood has been oxygenated in the lungs it travels back to the heart and is then pumped round the body. When blood reaches the various cells of the body, oxygen is transferred to them by the same method: the pressure of the oxygen in the blood is high whereas the pressure of the oxygen in the cells is low, so the oxygen passes into the cells. The amount of oxygen delivered depends on how busy the cell is. For example, more oxygen will be delivered to a muscle cell when it is exercising than when it is resting. The

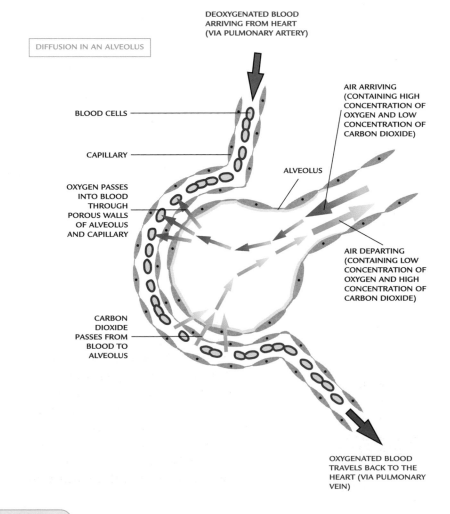

DIFFUSION IN AN ALVEOLUS

DEOXYGENATED BLOOD ARRIVING FROM HEART (VIA PULMONARY ARTERY)

AIR ARRIVING (CONTAINING HIGH CONCENTRATION OF OXYGEN AND LOW CONCENTRATION OF CARBON DIOXIDE)

BLOOD CELLS

CAPILLARY

ALVEOLUS

OXYGEN PASSES INTO BLOOD THROUGH POROUS WALLS OF ALVEOLUS AND CAPILLARY

AIR DEPARTING (CONTAINING LOW CONCENTRATION OF OXYGEN AND HIGH CONCENTRATION OF CARBON DIOXIDE)

CARBON DIOXIDE PASSES FROM BLOOD TO ALVEOLUS

OXYGENATED BLOOD TRAVELS BACK TO THE HEART (VIA PULMONARY VEIN)

blood delivers its oxygen and collects the carbon dioxide (pressure in the blood is lower than in the cells so the carbon dioxide passes into the blood), carrying it back to the lungs where it will be delivered to the alveoli and then exhaled.

How does blood travel to and from the lungs?

Via the pulmonary circulation which is the movement of blood from the heart to the lungs and back.

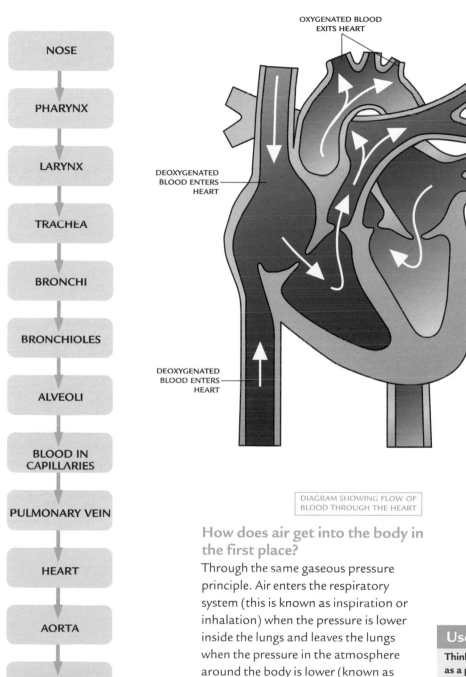

OXYGENATED BLOOD EXITS HEART

DEOXYGENATED BLOOD EXITS HEART TO LUNGS

OXYGENATED BLOOD ENTERS ATRIUM FROM LUNGS

DEOXYGENATED BLOOD ENTERS HEART

DEOXYGENATED BLOOD ENTERS HEART

DIAGRAM SHOWING FLOW OF BLOOD THROUGH THE HEART

| NOSE |
| PHARYNX |
| LARYNX |
| TRACHEA |
| BRONCHI |
| BRONCHIOLES |
| ALVEOLI |
| BLOOD IN CAPILLARIES |
| PULMONARY VEIN |
| HEART |
| AORTA |
| REST OF BODY (CELLS) |

OXYGEN'S ROUTE AROUND THE BODY

How does air get into the body in the first place?

Through the same gaseous pressure principle. Air enters the respiratory system (this is known as inspiration or inhalation) when the pressure is lower inside the lungs and leaves the lungs when the pressure in the atmosphere around the body is lower (known as expiration or exhalation). But it is the action of the muscles involved in respiration that make these changes in

Useful Tip

Think of internal respiration as a postal service delivering and collecting gases instead of letters. Oxygen is sent around the body, carbon dioxide is collected.

THE RESPIRATORY SYSTEM

pressure, and the movement of air, happen. The main muscle involved in the mechanics of respiration is the diaphragm which is helped by the intercostal muscles (positioned between the ribs).

SCHEMATIC DIAGRAM OF INHALATION AND EXHALATION

INHALATION

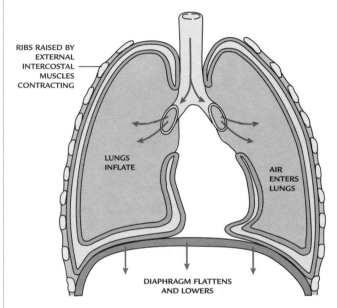

RIBS RAISED BY EXTERNAL INTERCOSTAL MUSCLES CONTRACTING

LUNGS INFLATE

AIR ENTERS LUNGS

DIAPHRAGM FLATTENS AND LOWERS

EXHALATION

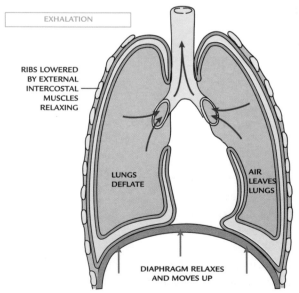

RIBS LOWERED BY EXTERNAL INTERCOSTAL MUSCLES RELAXING

LUNGS DEFLATE

AIR LEAVES LUNGS

DIAPHRAGM RELAXES AND MOVES UP

What is the diaphragm?

The diaphragm is a large muscle. It is positioned between the chest and abdomen and separates them from each other.

Structure: the diaphragm is made of a central sheet of tendon with muscle fibres towards the edges and it has three origins – posterior, lateral and anterior. When relaxed it is a dome shape; when contracted it flattens out.

Functions:

- inspiration/inhalation: when the diaphragm contracts, it flattens out and since it forms the bottom of the chest cavity, this cavity then increases in size and volume. This lowers the pressure inside the chest. Air is thus sucked in because the pressure is lower inside the body than outside.

- expiration/exhalation: when the diaphragm relaxes it becomes a dome shape and pushes up the chest cavity, thus reducing the cavity's size and volume and increasing the pressure. Air rushes out because the pressure is lower outside.

- the diaphragm also helps with expulsive body actions:
  - micturition (urine excretion)
  - defaecation (faeces explusion)
  - parturition (giving birth).

What are the intercostal muscles?

Intercostal muscles are between the ribs. These muscles aid the diaphragm in respiration. During inspiration the external intercostal muscles contract at the same time as the diaphragm, lifting the rib cage up and outwards. The flattened and lowered diaphragm and the raised ribs cause an increase in the size of the chest cavity. During expiration, the external intercostals relax allowing the ribs to fall down and inwards, helping to decrease the size of the chest cavity. Nerve impulses delivered by the intercostal nerves tell the muscles when to contract and relax.

How does the body know when to breathe?

Nerve cells called chemoreceptors, found in the aorta and carotid arteries (i.e. arteries which are very close to the heart) send impulses to the respiratory centre in the medulla oblongata of the brain with messages about the low levels of oxygen and high levels of carbon dioxide. When the level of carbon dioxide is too high and the level of oxygen too low a nerve impulse is sent to the diaphragm telling it to contract, thus causing inhalation. This is especially important during exercise and illness.

The brain's role in breathing

Two centres of the brain are involved – the respiratory centre in the medulla oblongata and the pons Varolii:

- the respiratory centre stimulates inspiration and controls the depth of breathing and its regularity
- the pons Varolii stops inspiration thus provoking expiration. When the respiratory centre tells the diaphragm to contract, air is sucked into the lungs, stimulating nerve cells called stretch receptors found in the lung tissue. These receptors send impulses to the pons Varolii which then sends impulses to the diaphragm telling it to relax, thus provoking expiration.

N.B. It is important to remember that breathing is not an intermittent process! The body does not stop breathing when the correct levels of oxygen and carbon dioxide are established, although breathing slows down and speeds up depending on our level of activity and health. Cells and tissues need to breathe all the time because every bodily function and movement requires oxygen and produces carbon dioxide. Breathing is a necessary and (in a healthy person) automatic function which continues throughout life.

What does air contain?

Air that comes into the body contains approximately 21% oxygen and 0.04% carbon dioxide whereas air that leaves the body contains approximately 15% oxygen and 4% carbon dioxide. Thus, the air we exhale contains 100 times more carbon dioxide and 6% less oxygen than the air we inhale.

You now know the structure and function of the respiratory system and how it is controlled by the nervous system. The final section of the chapter outlines the diseases and disorders of the respiratory system.

DISEASES AND DISORDERS

Bronchitis

Inflammation of the bronchial tubes which causes coughing, shortness of breath and fatigue. Causes include smoking and infections.

Emphysema

Alveoli stretch and lose their elasticity. This prevents effective breathing, causing cough, shortness of breath, and wheezing.

Pleurisy

Inflammation of the pleural lining; fluid may develop in pleura. Causes localised chest pain, shortness of breath, cough.

Pneumonia

Inflammation of lung tissue caused by infection. The lungs fill with fluid. Causes cough, fever, fatigue, headache and chest pain can be fatal.

Tuberculosis

Disease caused by bacteria, inhaled or eaten (in infected meat or milk). Symptoms include cough, night sweats and fever. BCG injections are used to vaccinate against it.

Asthma

Difficulty in exhalation, coughing and wheezing. Often caused by allergies.

Rhinitis

Stuffy, congested nose and sinuses. Caused by cold, flu, hay fever and sinus infections.

Hay fever

Allergic rhinitis; caused by allergy to certain pollens; symptoms include sneezing, runny nose and eyes and sometimes swelling/itching.

Sinusitis

Inflammation of sinuses, often following respiratory infection; causes headaches and facial pain.

Stress

Stress causes breathing rate to increase.

Interrelationships

Respiratory system links to:

Circulatory: the circulation transports oxygen from the respiratory system to every cell of the body and transports carbon dioxide to the respiratory system to be exhaled.

Nervous: respiration is closely controlled by the nervous system, which indicates when inhalation or exhalation should happen. Chemoreceptors in the main arteries stimulate the nervous response of the respiratory system to begin the process of inhaling oxygen when required.

Muscular: the intercostal muscles and diaphragm are fundamental to the process of respiration.

● SUMMARY

The respiratory system:
- *is a system for the exchange of gases from outside to inside the body and vice versa*
- *is controlled by the nervous system.*

The Urinary System

The urinary system filters blood and produces urine. It consists of the kidneys, ureters, bladder and urethra.

In Brief

The urinary system is one of the human body's waste disposal units its and filtration unit. Composed of the kidneys, ureters (tubes connecting kidneys to the bladder), bladder and urethra, this system helps to empty the body of potentially harmful waste substances, like urea and alcohol. It does so through filtration and excretion.

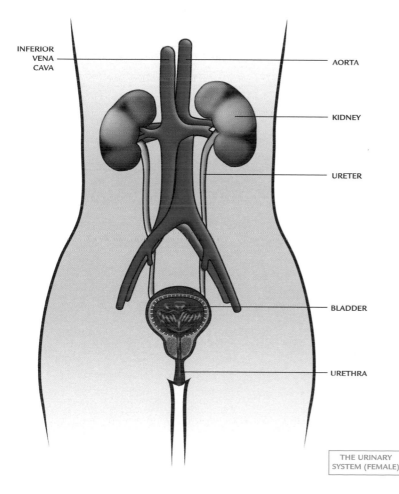

INFERIOR VENA CAVA

AORTA

KIDNEY

URETER

BLADDER

URETHRA

THE URINARY SYSTEM (FEMALE)

Learning objectives

The target knowledge of this chapter is:
- the structure of the urinary system
- the composition of urine
- diseases and disorders of the urinary system.

THE URINARY SYSTEM

STRUCTURE

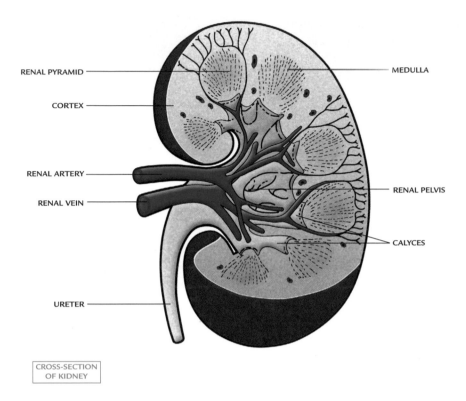

RENAL PYRAMID

CORTEX

RENAL ARTERY

RENAL VEIN

URETER

MEDULLA

RENAL PELVIS

CALYCES

CROSS-SECTION
OF KIDNEY

What is a kidney?

A kidney is a bean-shaped organ, about 11cm long. Humans have two of them, positioned on the posterior wall of the abdomen, either side of the spine, in the upper lumbar part of the back. On its way through the body about a quarter of the total blood in circulation passes through the kidneys in order to be filtered of toxic substances before re-circulating.

Structure: a kidney's structure has two distinct parts – the cortex on the outside and the medulla on the inside. The medulla leads into an area called the pelvis (sometimes called the renal pelvis). The concave centre of the kidney is known as the hilum and it is at this point that blood vessels, lymphatic

vessels, nerves and the ureter enter the organ. Kidney tissue is made up of over a million twisted tubes called nephrons, which do the kidneys' work of filtration and excretion.

Functions: to filter the blood, reabsorb useful materials needed by the body and form urine.

What is the (renal) pelvis?

Structure: the renal pelvis is a funnel-shaped cavity which connects the medulla to the ureter.

Function: it collects urine from the tubules in the medulla and passes it into the ureter.

What are ureters?

The tubes which connect the kidneys to the bladder.

Function: to take urine from the kidneys to the bladder. The presence of urine inside them stimulates a mechanical contraction which propels the fluid forwards.

What is the bladder?

Structure: sometimes called the urinary bladder this is a sac-like organ in the pelvic cavity.

Function: a reservoir for urine. When about 200ml of urine has been collected the presence of the liquid stimulates the autonomic nerve endings in the bladder wall and the walls contract. The bladder has an internal sphincter which relaxes when the walls contract, thus opening and emptying the urine into the urethra.

What is the urethra?

Structure: a narrow tube passing from the bladder to the outside of the body. It has an external sphincter which is voluntarily controlled by the central nervous system. It is shorter in women, thus making them more susceptible to infection.

Function: to take urine from inside the body (the bladder) to outside. In men, the urethra is also the passage for semen.

You now know the names of all the different parts of the urinary system and their individual functions. The next section explains the filtration of blood and the production of urine.

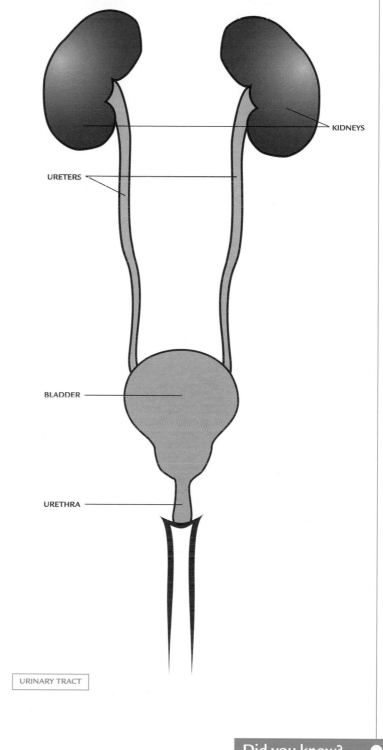

KIDNEYS

URETERS

BLADDER

URETHRA

URINARY TRACT

Did you know?

Eight large glasses per day is the recommended intake of water for a healthy body.

THE URINARY SYSTEM

The three stages of filtration and urine production

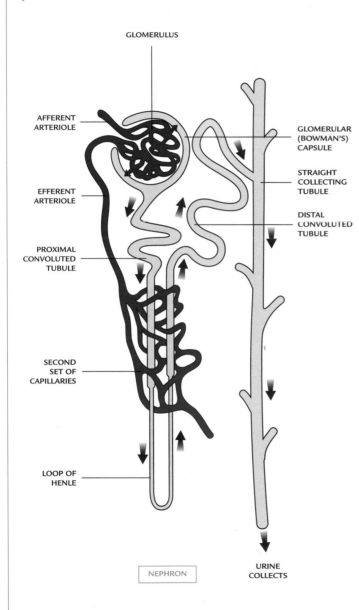

GLOMERULUS

AFFERENT ARTERIOLE

EFFERENT ARTERIOLE

PROXIMAL CONVOLUTED TUBULE

SECOND SET OF CAPILLARIES

LOOP OF HENLE

GLOMERULAR (BOWMAN'S) CAPSULE

STRAIGHT COLLECTING TUBULE

DISTAL CONVOLUTED TUBULE

NEPHRON

URINE COLLECTS

1) Filtration in the Bowman's capsule

Blood enters the kidneys via the afferent arterioles. These tiny blood vessels become the glomerulus, a tangle of capillaries surrounded by the glomerular capsule, also known as the Bowman's capsule. The blood in the capillaries is under pressure and since the capillary walls are permeable to water and other substances these pass through into the capsule, whilst blood cells and protein remain in the blood vessel. The Bowman's capsule thus serves as the collection point for the waste products carried in the blood. However, at this point the capsule has also collected other substances which are not waste and these will be reabsorbed as they pass through the nephron.

2) Re-absorption in the convoluted tubules

Once the filtered substances have been collected by the capsule they are passed into a system of twisted tubes, known as convoluted tubules. The tubes of the nephron which lead away from the Bowman's capsule are known as the proximal convoluted tubules. These straighten out into a long loop, called the Loop of Henle, which passes into the medulla and back to the cortex. Finally, there is another series of twists called the distal convoluted tubules. Reabsorption takes place in the tubules. Cells in the lining of the tubules are able to absorb any water, glucose, salts and ions which the body needs that must not be thrown away as waste. Only 1% of the liquid filtered into the Bowman's capsule is actually excreted as urine. The rest is re-absorbed.

3) Collection in the pelvic calyces

The nephron straightens out into a collecting tube in the medulla. These collecting tubes form masses called pyramids of the medulla, the tops of which stick up into the renal pelvis. The branches of the pelvis, or calyces, connect with the tops of these pyramids and collect the waste liquid, funneling it back into the pelvis, from where it will empty into the ureter.

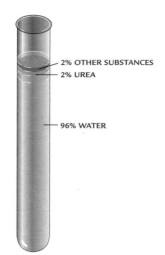

2% OTHER SUBSTANCES
2% UREA

96% WATER

COMPOSITION OF URINE

What is excreted: composition of urine

The liquid that results from the processes of filtration and reabsorption is known as urine. This amber-coloured liquid is composed of 96% water, 2% urea, and 2% other substances, such as ammonia, sodium, potassium, phosphates, chlorides, sulphates and excess vitamins. The salts must be excreted in order to maintain the correct balance of fluids and electrolytes in the body. The colour of urine comes from bilirubin, bile pigment. Normal urine is acidic, but this varies depending on diet and other factors.

Urine production

About 1.5 litres of urine is produced every 24 hours, which is only a small percentage compared to the amount of liquid filtered from the blood in the glomerulus. Urine production is increased by liquid intake and cold weather and decreased by drinking less and any activity or state that increases sweating (hot weather, exercise). Humans need a minimum of 0.5 litres of water per day for waste removal.

You now know how the urinary system works. The following section explains some of the diseases that affect it.

DISEASES AND DISORDERS

Cystitis

Inflammation of the bladder, causing pain when urinating. Sometimes caused by infections. Very common in women due in part to the shorter length of the female urethra.

Kidney stones

Deposits of substances found in urine which form solid stones within the renal pelvis, bladder or ureters. Extremely painful and often removed by surgery.

Nephritis or Bright's Disease

Inflammation of the kidney, resulting from causes other than infection. Often used to refer to a wide range of different inflammatory disorders.

Interrelationships

Urinary system links to:
Circulatory: the kidneys purify all the blood in the body.
Endocrine: the kidneys produce the enzyme renin which helps to regulate blood pressure as part of a system involving hormones.
Skeletal: the kidneys help to stimulate the production of bone marrow in the long bones.
Skin: the urinary system removes waste by excretion and therefore links to the other excretory system – the skin.

SUMMARY

The urinary system:
- *filters blood of potentially harmful substances*
- *produces urine through the processes of filtration and re-absorption*
- *excretes waste (urine).*

Index